The Level Land

Dola de Jong

THE LEVEL LAND

Drawings by PETER SPIER

CHARLES SCRIBNER'S SONS

NEW YORK

A-9.61 [J]

PRINTED IN THE UNITED STATES OF AMERICA

Library of Congress Catalog Card Number 61–14768

TO MY FATHER,

In memoriam

Preface

WHEN I'm asked which one of my books for children I like best, I don't have to think very long. I can come right out with the answer: *The Level Land* is my favorite book for young people.

You can imagine how delighted I am that a little more than ten years after the last printing, the book is available again. There it is, in a new cheerful coat and jacket, with different letters and pictures and with a bigger and better glossary. To tell you the truth, I like the new edition better than the old one, just as I like a new dress more than one that I have worn for several seasons.

The answer to the question of which is my favorite book ties right in with that other question authors are asked frequently: Why did you write that book?

Before the Second World War, I was one of those people in Holland, who, like Miep in the book, was very much aware of the threat of war. Quite a while before it happened I realized that the Nazi government in Germany would stop at nothing in its desire for conquest of all of Europe. And I also was quite sure that the small countries, however determined they were to defend themselves, wouldn't have a chance to withstand the German army. I was also convinced just like Miep, about whom you're going to read, that the Jews of Holland like the Jews in Eastern and Middle Europe before them, would become the helpless victims of Hitler's insane and cruel persecution of minorities.

So, I left Holland and made my way, via North Africa, to the United States. By the time I arrived here, America had entered the war and all communications between this country and the continent of Europe had come to a halt. For years I didn't know what had happened to the members of my family in Holland. Had they fled? Were they in hiding? Were they still alive? I thought about them all the time and about Holland, my native country. And the way it goes with writers, I started to write about Holland and about a Dutch family, just to ease my concern and to feel closer to all I had left behind.

In other words, the Van Oordt family of this book helped me through the war. Although this family came out of my imagination and none of its members ever existed, every one of them bears a resemblance to someone in my background. I have even caught myself forgetting that the Van Oordt family actually never existed. They've become good friends of mine, just as they became friends of many young people in this and other countries. I just hope that after reading my story you will feel the same way. It's a good feeling....

Dola de Jong

Contents

THE VAN OORDT FAMILY

Moeder (Mooder)
Vader (Vaader)
Miep (Meep)
Jaap (Yaahp)
Jan (Yahn)
Ruth (Rut)
Pieter Pim (Peter Pim)
Anne
Geesje (Gheasjé)

Chapter 1

ALL OF THEM

THEY were having lunch, five of the six Van Oordt children. Miep, the oldest girl, who was eighteen, presided at the table.

"You may have two slices of buttered bread with nothing else on them, and after that you may eat on your bread whatever you want," Miep told four-year-old Pieter Pim, who was very busy sprinkling chocolate shavings on his bread, more and more shavings, a very fat layer. All the while he murmured, "This is nothing, nothing, nothing, nothing at all."

The two other boys, Jan, who was thirteen, and Jaap, three years older, laughed. So did Ruth, but Miep tried to remain serious. "Pieter Pim, you know the rules. Two slices with just butter before the trimmings."

Pieter Pim hastened to put part of his sandwich in his mouth, and protested, "But that's what I'm doing. There *is* butter on my sandwich, between the bread and the chocolate. See." His fat rosy cheeks were pushed out twice their size with the effort to chew the big bite he had taken.

Now Miep couldn't help but laugh too, and Pieter Pim looked contentedly around. Everything was in fine shape. Even Miep laughed.

"He's going to be a handful. He's not our baby any more, and he won't like that," eleven-year-old Ruth said.

"Is that so, Miss Know-it-all," exclaimed Vader, who just then walked into the dining room. All at once there was quite an uproar, because they all recognized the two packages he carried.

"Rusks with *muisjes*," shouted Ruth. She had known they would get this treat, the traditional treat in Holland when a baby is born.

"Oh, boy! . . ." Jan yelled, slapping Jaap on the shoulder in excitement.

"Take it easy. . . ." Jaap muttered with the dignity of his age. However, his eyes were on the box of rusks and on the small bag with sugared anise seeds Vader put beside his plate.

"Is there any hot food for me?" Vader asked Miep. He pretended not to notice the cries and eager looks of the children. "My, but I'm hungry. First I'm going to have my lunch in peace." He spoke in a serious tone of voice, but there was a twinkle in his eyes.

"Please, Vader," Ruth begged.

"Come on, Dad, let's have it," Jan shouted.

"Stop teasing, Vader," Jaap grumbled.

"I've had a hectic morning," Vader went on, ignoring them. "Were there any messages, Miep?"

"You saw them on the telephone pad. Don't play dumb, Vader." Ruth looked at him with reproachful eyes.

"What's in the little bag and in the box?" Pieter Pim wanted to know.

"Rusks and *muisjes*, stupid," Jan said.

"Now, how is he supposed to know that?" Ruth seemed quite indignant.

"Because when he was born we had them too," said Jan. "I remember very well."

Now they all burst out laughing. "That's a good

one," shouted Jaap. "When he was born we had them too. . . . That's a good one. And when you were born I suppose you got one, in your cradle!"

"Sstttt," Vader warned, "you'll wake Moeder." He pushed the packages over to Miep. Taking a large dish from the sideboard, she started to prepare the treat. She spread the rusks with a thick layer of butter and sprinkled the *muisjes* on them, pink *muisjes*, because a little sister had been born. If it had been a boy, the *muisjes* would have been white. All the children were happy about the birth of their new sister. Jan didn't show it, but he was as pleased as the others, and already saw himself, just as Ruth and Jaap did, playing with the little creature, and protecting it. Only Pieter Pim wasn't so very enthusiastic. It was so strange, that little red thing in the cradle; and he didn't like it at all that Moeder was in bed and didn't concern herself with him in the least. That strange woman with the white cap had sent him out of the room, and Miep was home and bossed everybody in the house.

"Well, I don't care," Pieter Pim thought. "I'll show them." Nobody but Moeder could tell him what to do; sometimes Vader could, when he was home and there were no patients waiting for him. Then, too, there was Geesje in the big old-fashioned kitchen, with all the shining brass. But Geesje let him do everything he wanted, except on Fridays, when she scrubbed the floor. And she called him Jan Stavast, which is a marvelous name for a Dutch boy. It stands for everything that's fine and strong and courageous. And Pieter Pim was fine, strong and courageous. Yes, indeed!

The only thing to be heard for some time was the crunching of the rusks, the grating sound that the small round sweets made between the teeth, and the voice of Vader who was telling Miep about his morning visits. Miep was interested in all Vader's experiences. She was at the School for Social Work in Amsterdam, and later on she planned to help Vader with his patients.

And Miep knew how to help! After receiving Vader's telegram she had immediately made the journey home from Amsterdam, in the northwest, to the Veluwe, in the center of Holland. However, she didn't really understand how Moeder managed to have everything run so smoothly. Four children at home, and now another baby, and the housekeeping, and Vader's practice. There were messages to be taken the whole day; the waiting-room and the consulting-room had to be kept clean; and always the muddy feet of the patients in the marble hall.

"I wish they would walk in on their hands," Gees would say. "You just can't teach them to wipe their feet. In my time, we put our *klompen* at the front door, but the country children of today would rather wear leather shoes. Wooden shoes aren't good enough for them, which is nonsense, for your feet stay much warmer in them."

"Come, come, Gees," Moeder would say, "times are changing. Now that leather shoes are made in factories, they are much cheaper than they used to be, and why shouldn't the farmers' children have them? . . . They can play and run more comfortably in them."

"But *klompen* give them strong feet," said Gees.

"That's true," Moeder admitted.

And then Gees went back for the hundredth time to scrub the hall and to polish the brass bell, because things had to be clean. As long as Gees had worked for the doctor's family, and that was all of fifteen years now, the house had been spic and span, inside and out, and she intended to keep it that way. The red bricks on the outside up to where she could reach with her scrubber, the dark-green window sills, the little brick path through the garden to the front door, the corridor, even they shone with cleanliness. And the bell . . . you could use it for a mirror!

The house was called "The Level Land." It was old-fashioned and cozy, and it stood on guard at the edge of the great flat heath, like a faithful mother with a large lap.

Besides all her other activities, Moeder helped Vader in the dispensary. For simple examinations and the usual medicine the people didn't have to go to town. This, of course, added a lot to the work, and when the children were in bed at last, Moeder and Vader often worked late into the night. "There the doctor is, brewing something or other again," the farmers said as they came from "The Gilt Arms" at night, and saw the Laboratory light shining over the heath. The Laboratory . . . that certainly was a high-sounding name for the small barn where Vader prepared mixtures and did blood tests. But although it was only a small barn, the children were strictly forbidden to enter, and ever since Pieter Pim could walk, Moeder had kept the key in the little key basket which she always carried with her around the house.

You had to keep an eye on Pieter Pim. That boy was always wandering about, trying to find the ins and outs of everything.

Now he slipped away from the table unnoticed, and walked into Moeder's room. He really had good intentions; he wanted to let Moeder and the new little sister taste the rusk because he had noticed that Miep hadn't saved any for them.

It was very quiet in the room. Moeder was sleeping with her head deep in the pillow. Zwart, the very black cat, had stolen into the room, and lay at Moeder's feet. The strange woman had taken off her white cap, and now she looked, thought Pieter Pim, twice as strange asleep in a chair near Moeder's dressing-table. He tiptoed over to the lovely cradle with the pink bows, and peeped over the edge at the new little sister.

Although Pieter didn't care very much for his new sister, he really felt sorry for her, lying there all alone without anybody paying attention to her. Instead of playing with her, the grown-up people went to sleep. The children in the living room got tasty rusks with *muisjes*, to celebrate the birth of the little sister, and the little sister herself got nothing. That is, thought Pieter, if it hadn't been for him. And so he took a foot-stool, very quietly, of course, so Moeder wouldn't wake up, and started to feed the little sister rusk with *muisjes*.

Then all kinds of things happened very quickly, and before Pieter Pim realized what was going on, he was standing between Vader's knees in the consulting-room, sniffing violently to keep back the tears.

"Look, Pieter Pim," said Vader, "now Moeder has another little child . . ."

"Who from? . . ." Pieter asked, because that was something he had wanted to ask all along.

"From the good Lord," said Vader. "Only the good Lord can give something so beautiful."

" 'Course," said Pieter seriously, "nobody else could pay for such a beautiful thing."

"Quite right," nodded Vader, "but listen, Pieter; now that little sister has come, you have a new job. You have to protect her, and you won't ever do such things again as you did just now. Giving a hard rusk to a very tiny baby, that doesn't even have teeth! A big boy, as you are now, thinks before he does something like that."

"How silly of me," said Pieter, disgusted. "I should've soaked that rusk in milk first, shouldn't I, Vader?"

And then Vader suddenly had to look for something in his desk very urgently and didn't answer, and so Pieter continued: "But that strange lady didn't have to get so mad because of that, did she, Vader?"

"Well, Pieter, the nurse loves the little baby and she was afraid that you would hurt it."

"No, *sir*," said Pieter, "I wouldn't ever hurt the little sister. She can take walks with me, when it's summer. It is too cold now, isn't it, Vader?"

"Much too cold," said Vader. "We had a good frost last night, and we'll soon be able to skate."

"Me, too?" asked Pieter.

"You, too, because now you belong to the big children."

And so Pieter Pim walked to the kitchen as proud as a peacock, to tell Gees that he was going to skate, too, you just wait and see!

And Vader hurriedly called in the first patient from the waiting-room; it was farmer Jelgers, looking like a thundercloud for he had already waited much too long for his liking.

Chapter 2

JAN

YES, THE FIRST FROST of the year had come. There was snow in the air and the big fleecy clouds hung low over the countryside. Like a large cotton quilt, thought Jan, who was walking home over the hard-frozen heath-road.

After school he walked along the pond on the baron's estate to see if the ice was thick enough yet. But the forester of the estate had had big holes cut for the ducks. Now they were swimming around restlessly or marching on stiff legs between the holes.

Jan was angry with the baron. It was such a long time every year before he opened the rink to the villagers. First he kept the holes open until he had put up the ducks elsewhere, and only then did the men come to stretch the ropes and to prepare the illumination for the night, and at last the little *koek* booths were put up and the flags raised. If they started all that the day after tomorrow, they would be finished in five days at the earliest. Jan decided to go and skate on the ditch first, at least if it wasn't going to snow.

He jerked his school-bag up under his other arm. How heavy the darn thing was again, and that miserable homework! It didn't help him a bit anyway, working like a slave. He was behind in his work. In the beginning of the year he hadn't done a thing, he had only just made the H.B.S., yes, with a make-up exam. Now things were all wrong. He would never be able to catch up again, and the principal had sent for him and had said that he'd better change to the M.U.L.O., the continuation school. When you had finished that, your studies were over. You were admitted to the University only if you graduated from the High School.

He hadn't told anybody. It had been very embarrassing and he had felt terribly small, there in the principal's room.

"It's a pity, Jan," the principal had said. "If you don't

become a doctor, it will be a great disappointment to your father. For how many generations have there been doctors in your family?"

"Four, Meneer," Jan had said, and suddenly it had become clear to him how grave the situation really was. All of a sudden, as if a curtain were lifted in front of him, he had understood the sorrow this would cause his Vader. Vader's great-great-grandfather had been a doctor, and ever since there had always been one son in the family who had taken over the practice; it was a tradition. Vader often talked about how it would be, when Jan came back from Leiden—because it was at Leiden where they had all studied, the oldest University in the country—and how Jan, after his internship at the hospital at Arnhem, where Vader had also worked, would come home and gradually take over Vader's practice. Vader was always very happy when he talked about that time. He would draw at his pipe and talk long and loudly, so that Moeder had to warn him that he would awaken the little ones, upstairs in bed.

How could Jan ever tell him what the principal had said? At first he had tried to catch up with his work, but it was so much that he didn't know where to start, and at school they kept going ahead . . . geometry, algebra, German, French . . . no, it seemed hopeless.

When he had crossed the heath, and passed the corner, he saw two lights burning in the house. One was upstairs in Moeder's bedroom, and he was glad there was one in the living room too, as usual. Miep would be sitting behind the tea-table, in Moeder's place, and would be waiting for the children to come home from school.

Jan ran till he got to the front door. He brushed aside Kees, the big shepherd dog, who wanted to play. Suddenly he longed terribly for the living room, for the warm light that shone through the yellow silk lamp-shade and blended with the red glow from the stove, the spicy smell of the tea, brewing on the little spirit-stove, and for Miep, who would remove the tea-cozy from the pot, as soon as he came in, and would say, "Quick, take off your coat, there are freshly baked cookies, they're still warm, here, the first cup is for Moeder, you bring it up, but take care that you don't wake the baby, didn't you see Ruth on the way, Jaap has his organ lesson," all in one breath, because she wanted so much to make everything just as cozy and warm as it was when Moeder poured the tea.

Moeder was sitting up in bed, mending socks and she looked up with a smile when Jan came in with the tea.

"Are you sure that Vader allows you to mend socks in bed?" asked Jan anxiously.

Moeder laughed. "I didn't ask him, you know. Look, the whole basket is full of mending. It couldn't just stay that way, could it, until I get up again?"

"That's true." Jan lay down full length across the foot of the bed.

"Tired, Jan?"

"No, not a bit."

"Something wrong? You're so quiet. Don't you feel well?" Moeder asked.

Jan sat upright. "Yes," he said quickly, afraid that Moeder would notice something. Ever since he had talked with the principal, it seemed to him that he was deceiving everyone at home. Usually they knew everything about each other and now he had this secret. And he couldn't possibly tell. Or could he tell Moeder? Maybe she would know what to do. Would she let him be tutored, as many other children were? Vader was against it. He didn't think it was necessary.—"If you can't keep up, through no fault of your own, then you have to repeat the same class. It's good for you. And if it is because you've been lazy, well, then it's your business to see that you make up for it. I won't spend money on that."—That's what he had said, when Miep was cramming so hard for her final exam. It would be lovely, Jan thought, if he could tell his troubles to Moeder. He put his hands deep inside his trouser pockets. He felt that Moeder was waiting for an answer. But at that moment Ruth came in.

"It's snowing," Ruth said. "It just started."

Jan walked to the window and pushed aside the net curtains. Large flakes were whirling down, so he couldn't even see the lights of the village any more.

"It's dry snow," said Ruth. "It's sticking to the ground."

"Now we can't skate," Jan grumbled, but Pieter Pim danced into the room and sang at the top of his voice, "It's snowing, it's snowing, Moeder, come and look, it's snowing!"

"You three go drink your tea. Miep is waiting," advised Moeder. "I'll have a little rest before dinner."

That evening the meal was already over when Vader came home. He looked tired and was chilled to the bone. The old Chevrolet convertible didn't close too well and the cutting wind that blew over the heath whistled through the seams and cracks. Geesje had warmed up the kale mashed with potatoes and had saved a big piece of sausage; "farmer's cabbage" they called that dish.

"Gosh, I wish I could stay quietly at home for a change," Vader said.

"You should go to bed early for once, doctor," Gees said. "You haven't been home one single night all week. They call you out for every little ache." Gees was always angry with Vader's patients if they sent for him at night. The people were glad when it was Moeder, who came to the door. She didn't argue with them.

A little later, just when Vader was settled comfortably with the evening paper, the doctor's bell boomed throughout the hall and they heard Gees' persuasive voice at the door. Soon she came in. She looked serious.

"There you go again, doctor," she said. "You'd better go quickly. It's the elder son of Aldewaal's. His father has had a fall. The boy ran all the way over."

"Well, so be it." Vader put the paper down with a regretful face. "I wonder what's happening in the world. I haven't read the paper thoroughly for weeks. All I know is what my patients tell me."

"The less you hear about it, the better," grumbled Gees. "There's nothing to laugh about. That war is horrible. I can't read the paper, it makes me sick."

"If only we stay out of it," Vader said.

"Oh, we're sure to. The Germans won't dare to come here. They know quite well how strong we are."

"Let's hope so," Miep said, but she did not seem so sure of it.

Vader looked at her in amazement. "Do you doubt it at all, Miep?"

"I'm convinced they *will* invade us. Why not?"

"You're crazy," Jaap flared up. "Do you hear that silly stuff in Amsterdam?"

"Let's not quarrel about it, children. I hope I'm wrong." Miep started to clear the table. She knew quite well that people thought the things she said were absurd. Everybody here laughed at her, yet there were people in Amsterdam who had the same fears.

When Vader went to get his bag from the consulting-room, Jan followed him. "Shall I go along with you, Vader? It's so dark on the road and now with the snow . . . I can wipe the snow from your windshield so that you can see. Your windshield wipers aren't much good."

"Have you finished your homework?"

"I'll get up at six o'clock tomorrow morning," Jan promised. It seemed a godsend to him to go now with Vader. He wouldn't have to tackle the pile of books on the table in his den, his homework that he couldn't manage anyway. And maybe he would find the courage, on the way back when they would be alone, to talk about his problems.

It was pitch-dark on the heath, and the snow reflected the headlights with so much glare that Vader found it difficult to keep his eyes on the road. Jan had to keep getting out to wipe the windshield. They drove very slowly.

"You couldn't drive faster, could you, doctor?" asked Henk Aldewaal, who sat in the back. "Vader was in bad pain when I left. I'm afraid he's broken his leg. He's still lying in the barn, for we didn't dare pick him up. Keep them lying down is what they tell you in the Boy Scouts' first aid booklet and that's what I did."

"Well done," Vader nodded, satisfied. "I'm sorry, my boy, but I don't dare to drive faster. Can't you feel the back wheels slip? If we should slide off the bank we couldn't get the car back on the road, and it would take hours before we could help your father."

"Could you manage it just a little bit faster?" asked Jan, who felt very sorry for Henk.

His father didn't answer, but the boys noticed that he stepped on the accelerator a little harder.

The snow started to fall more and more densely and the wind became stronger every minute.

"I don't understand how you could find your way to us, Henk," said the doctor.

"It wasn't snowing so hard then and I have my flash-light from the air raid precaution service with me."

"May I see it?" asked Jan.

Henk passed him the flashlight and Jan played the light over the heath and on the road bank. "I know what, Vader," he suddenly cried. "I'll stand on the running board and I'll use the flashlight for a headlight."

"Nothing doing," said the doctor. "It's much too dangerous."

"It isn't dangerous, Vader. I'll hold on. We'll let the window down and Henk can sit next to you and hold my arm."

The doctor drove on without answering, but when they had crossed the open plain and were on the path along the wood to Aldewaal's farm, he stopped and said, "Well, come on then, Jan. I can't see the side of the road any more. Those trees make it twice as dark. But be careful, won't you?"

Jan wiped off the windshield once more, and then he stepped on to the running board, with the flashlight in his right hand, while he clung to the door with his left.

"That makes a big difference," said the doctor gratefully, and Jan felt very glad that he could be helpful. Fortunately they hadn't far to go, and after a short while, Vader carefully turned in through the gate of the farm and drove up the drive.

Vrouw Aldewaal, in spite of the blizzard, was outside looking for them. She was a large woman with a hard face, but she almost cried with relief when Vader stepped out of the car.

"My husband is in the barn, doctor. I think it's a shame, but the boy said we had to leave him there. He said he had learned that from the Boy Scouts. Aldewaal is good and mad, doctor, that we didn't carry him inside, but I said the boy learned it, it's in the First Aid booklet, and you just stay where you are."

In the meantime they had arrived at the barn. Jan handed the bag to his father and returned to the car to throw the blanket over the radiator.

"Shouldn't you put on some dry clothes?" Henk asked Jan. "I can give you a coat of mine."

"No, thanks. First we've got to help Vader."

In the barn they found the doctor kneeling beside Aldewaal, who had apparently been reassured about having been left there. At least he didn't utter another sound, even when the doctor slit open his trouser-leg.

"It seems a shame to do that," said vrouw Aldewall, "If only you had worn your old trousers!"

"If only we knew everything beforehand," said Vader. "But there it is, we don't know what's in store for us, vrouw Aldewaal. It would be nice if you would go in and make a cup of strong hot coffee for Aldewaal, that'll do him good, and we could do with a little, too."

When the farmer's wife had disappeared, Jan helped his father as well as he could, and, with the aid of the farm hands, they carefully carried Aldewaal inside.

The farmer moaned and groaned when they laid him down in the old-fashioned cupboard-bed. He seemed to be in much pain.

"I'll give you something for the pain now," said the doctor, "but I do want to take you to the hospital in town this very evening. Your leg will be properly set, Aldewaal. The fracture is just near the knee and it's better that we mend it right now and mend it well than have to do it all over again later on."

"I won't go to the hospital," said the farmer. "I've never been in one in my whole life and I'm not going now. You just set the leg here, doctor. That's good enough for me."

"But not for me, Aldewaal. I'm your doctor and I'm

responsible. Come on, man, be sensible. You're a modern farmer, you've got a tractor, you're the president of the cooperative . . . now be a little progressive about your body, too. I can't guarantee anything; if I have to set it here, there's a good chance that you'll have to walk around with a crooked leg later on. You know me quite well by now, Aldewaal; I don't exaggerate. If I say that I think it's necessary, then it's necessary."

After a good deal of persuasion from the woman and Henk, the farmer let himself be carried to the car, where they made him as comfortable as they could. Henk went along with his father. He would spend the night at the doctor's house, but vrouw Aldewaal had to stay home, for the farm's activities started again the next morning at six o'clock, and they couldn't do without her.

And so, a little while later, they started on their way to Arnhem.

"Once we're on the main road, Aldewaal, it'll be less bumpy," promised the doctor. He drove as carefully as he could. Jan again stood on the running board and lighted the road with his torch. And while Jan was standing there and was concentrating all his attention on the road before him, he suddenly knew with great certainty that he must become a doctor. In all these months when he had been thinking more about football and hockey and skating than about his work, he hadn't really understood what he was throwing away. Now, suddenly, he knew that he wanted to be a doctor, not to keep up a tradition, but because he himself *wanted* it. When he had helped his father there in the barn, when he passed him the splints and the bandages, in the most skillful way he could think of, and looked at his father's hands doing their work so efficiently, when he listened to the sober but persuasive words he spoke, he suddenly knew that he wanted to be like his father, that there was nothing in the world that he would rather be.

Chapter 3

WERNER

IT WAS LATE when they arrived at the hospital. Henk had fallen asleep on the way, and even Aldewaal was dozing now and then. When he woke up he asked what time it was.

But Jan kept watch, and helped his father keep a look-out on the road. It had stopped snowing, and they were guided by the distant town lights that twinkled now on the left, now on the right, with each turn of the road. It was becoming colder and colder. The snow had gradually changed into an icy crust, not only because of the frost, but also with the pressure of the countless cars and trucks that drove to Germany along this road.

"Well, doctor," said the night porter when they finally reached the hospital, "it certainly looks as if you maintain a regular night service between the Veluwe and the town."

"That's the village doctor's job, my friend," the doctor said. He disappeared into the large building to give instructions for Aldewaal's admission, and sent the boys into the waiting-room.

"Whew, what a smell," whispered Henk when they walked over the long, dimly lighted corridor. But Jan sniffed the hospital smell with pleasure and suddenly he had a vision of his room and the stack of books that was waiting for him. The books definitely seemed less thick than they were in reality. At the same time he knew that tomorrow morning when he opened them they would be as bulky as ever, and full of things he didn't know and didn't remember. But he would go to the principal and tell him that he did want to be a doctor, and ask him if he could show him how he could catch up with his class.

There was another boy in the waiting-room. When

Jan and Henk came in, he jumped to his feet and made a sort of bow to the boys. What a funny fellow, thought Jan, and he could see that Henk made the same remark to himself. The strange boy looked at him for a moment, and when he saw that Jan and Henk took some magazines from the table in the center of the room he, too, sat down. Jan pretended to be engrossed in his reading, but he couldn't help looking at the strange boy again. Something had aroused his curiosity. That fellow looked different from himself and Henk. What was he doing here in the waiting-room so late? Maybe he was waiting while his father or mother was being operated upon; maybe he was terrified. He looked so pale, sort of cheesy, Jan thought, none too kindly. He was dressed in a suit like a grownup, but still you could see that he wasn't any older than Jan. It looked as if he were going to sleep, for he had closed his eyes and he slowly sagged down in his chair.

The boys looked through the magazines as fast as they could. You didn't get hold of these every day and they had a lot of interesting pictures of the invasion of Poland and Czechoslovakia, pictures of warships and tanks.

Jan hoped that his father would stay away for a while longer. He was enjoying the magazines.

But the doctor returned quite soon. He came in with a nurse and to Jan's astonishment they walked straight up to the strange boy. "*Dies ist Werner, Doktor,*" said the nurse and she put a hand on the boy's shoulder. Oh, a *Mof*, thought Jan when he heard the nurse speaking German. Nowadays everybody called the Germans *Mof*, a bad name for them, but what it really meant Jan didn't know. In the meantime the nurse had introduced the doctor to Werner and the doctor in turn called the boys and said in German, "Werner, this is my son Jan and this is Henk Aldewaal; if you don't mind I'll take you home with me in my car. Then you can stay with us until your fellow-traveller is well again."

The boy looked from the doctor to the nurse; he didn't seem quite at ease, so the nurse said kindly, "Werner, you just go along with the doctor. I'm sure you'll like it a lot there, and a few days of rest and solid food will do you good."

The boy laughed a little, shyly. Suddenly—he didn't know why—Jan felt sorry for him, but still he couldn't think of anything to say to put him at his ease. His German was nothing to shout about, they had just started it at school.

Henk left for a moment to say good-bye to his father, and while they were waiting for him in the car, the the doctor talked to Werner. He didn't ask him any questions at all, which amazed Jan a little—where did that fellow come from and what was he doing in the hospital—but talked about the weather, and the slippery road and about the *boterhammen* they were going to eat, when they got home, so that the boy didn't have to answer at all.

They drove back silently. Werner sat huddled in a corner in the back, and Henk, a little rigid, sat next to him, at the other window. Jan noticed that his father was deep in serious thought. He smoked continuously, which he always did at such times.

When they were about half-way home, Henk suddenly said, "Doctor, you'd better stop. I think that Werner is sick." The doctor turned to look and then he stopped and helped the boy out of the car.

Henk and Jan looked at each other. "I'm sure he is a refugee," said Henk. "How, why? . . ." asked Jan to whom that hadn't occurred at all.

"A Jewish refugee, probably," said Henk. "They come over the border regularly. My uncle Berend has a farm near Oldenzaal, at the German border; and when we were there the other day, he showed us the paths in the woods, where they cross. My uncle saw several of them. . . ."

"And what about the customs officers?" asked Jan.

"I don't know. They don't catch all the smugglers who take coffee and tea and chocolate over the border, either, do they?"

They sat waiting in silence, till the doctor brought Werner back. He wrapped him in a rug and let him sit with him in front.

It was after midnight when they came home, but

there was motherly Miep waiting up for them with a pile of bread and butter and hot chocolate. She didn't even look amazed when Henk and Werner walked into the living room. Apparently Vader had telephoned her. She had prepared a folding cot in Jan's room, for Werner, and had made up a bed on the couch in the living room for Henk.

Werner didn't want anything to eat. Vader made him take some medicine and sent him immediately off to bed.

After that Vader told Miep what he knew about the boy, so that Jan and Henk could also hear it. Werner's parents had sent him away from Germany with an uncle, who fled from the country in his car. They had succeeded in crossing the border, but then they had to abandon the car somewhere, for lack of money with which to buy gas. They had walked to Arnhem, which was more than twenty-five kilometers; then the uncle couldn't go any farther and a truck driver had picked them up and brought them to the hospital. It appeared that the uncle was seriously ill. He had caught a cold on the way and his lungs were affected. Since it was so late at night, the nurses hadn't quite known what to do with the boy. Just when they had decided to give him a room in the hospital until they could deal with the matter next morning, the doctor had offered to take Werner home and keep him as long as it was necessary. The nurses gratefully accepted the offer.

"It's a sad world," Vader concluded his story.

"But why did Werner have to flee, Vader?" asked Jan.

"Well, my boy, if I had been Werner's father, I would have wanted him to do the same thing. In this way the boy has at least a chance for the future, which the Germans won't give him." Then the doctor sent him off to bed and Jan tiptoed into his room, where he quietly undressed in the dark.

Chapter 4

RUTH

JAAP RODE to the village on his bicycle with Ruth sitting behind him on the luggage-carrier. It was hard work, bicycling against the wind. The bicycle careened over the road. Ruth clasped Jaap's belt with both hands. Her feet propped up on either side of the back wheel, kept sliding off, and she had cramps in her calves. Every-time Jaap rode over a hole she bounced back on the iron luggage-carrier, and not very gently either! No, it wasn't exactly fun, there on the back of the bike. And it was awfully cold, so early in the morning. But Ruth was in a hurry, in a great hurry. She had to catch the train to town. Her heart thumped when she thought of it. Jaap, who also took that train to school, mustn't guess it. She must pretend that she was going to the village school, but when Jaap put her down there she would have to run to the station, to catch the train. She couldn't wait on the platform, no, but in the waiting room until everybody had got in, and then she would have to run to the last car. Suppose the boys should see her! Above all Jan mustn't.

It was just because of Jan that she was doing all this.

She had no idea what excuse she would give at school, that afternoon, for staying out in the morning. She couldn't say she'd been sick, for then the teacher would ask for a note from her mother. The best thing would be to pretend that she just hadn't felt like going to school. She would certainly get a sound punishment, maybe even be sent to the principal. Just imagine! Playing hookey was indeed one of the worst things you could do at school. It hardly ever happened. Once in a while a boy would do it, in the summer when the weather was fine. But a girl didn't play hookey. Ruth had a funny feeling in the pit of her stomach. She had never done a thing like that before. And although she knew that it was for a good cause, involving somebody else, she still didn't feel easy. What would the girls say? Elly, for instance, who was the smartest and prettiest girl in her class. Not because she really *was*, Ruth thought, but because she thought so herself, and was so sure about it. But she wasn't really nice; she was conceited, and high-handed with girls who were shy, or less clever than she was. Elly would say, "Silly, who plays hookey anyway?" And Ruth wouldn't be able to defend herself. She was a little afraid of Elly.

Besides, nobody must know why she had stayed away. That was her secret. . . .

"Jaap! . . ." Ruth shouted against the wind.

But Jaap didn't hear her. She pulled at his belt.

"Don't pull like that, Ruth! . . ." Jaap shouted to the back. "Sit still!"

"Jaap . . . listen. . . ."

"What?"

"You can let me off a little nearer. The Main Road will be all right. I have to do something else first!"

When Jaap had deposited her, Ruth looked after him. How nice Jaap was, Ruth thought. Really much nicer than Jan. But she loved Jan more. That was a funny thing. Jan often growled at her. Sometimes they had terrific rows, and they fought each other. He teased her and was a nuisance and played jokes on her, yet she liked him more than Jaap. Jan would romp around and tell jokes, and sometimes bring her presents. Or he would be "low" as he called it, and he would come to her little room and sit there sighing and grumbling. When she tried to comfort him he would push her away. . . .

Oh, Jaap was different. He talked very little. He was always working, and devoted all his spare time to the piano. It was just as if Jaap had a little house around him, a little house of glass. You could see him, but you couldn't get very near. Sometimes when you were telling him something, he would say, "Is that so?" very absent-mindedly, and then you felt as if you had said something very silly. It wasn't because Jaap was already sixteen years old. Miep was eighteen, and yet you could talk and laugh with her. But it was because Jaap was *different.*

These were all the things Ruth was thinking about while she was running to the station.

Yesterday, in the early morning, Jan had come to her with all his books. He had gone with Vader the night before and had done nothing about his homework.

"Why don't you do it in your own room?" Ruth, who was writing in her secret diary, had asked.

"There's a boy in my room," Jan told her. "He's still sleeping and I don't want to wake him up."

"What? . . ."

"Ssssstt! Don't yell like that, you'll wake everybody."

Then Jan had told her about Werner. Ruth wanted to know all the details, but Jan snapped at her. He had to work.

Well, that working of Jan's didn't amount to much, anyway. He opened first one book, then another. He grumbled and sighed, and fidgeted so that Ruth had to laugh to herself.

But then, all of a sudden, he had pushed his chair

back so forcibly that it fell, and brushed all the books and papers from the small table with a sweep of his arm. He went to the window and stood with his hands in his pockets. It had really upset Ruth, though she knew quite well that Jan would run out if she tried to comfort him.

At last he sat down on the edge of her bed and had told her secret. How he was so far behind at school and about what the principal had said to him. Also that the night before when he was helping Vader to put Aldewaal's leg in splints, he had realized how stupid he had been to be so lazy, because more than anything he wanted to become a doctor.

"Do you think it will seem funny if I go to the principal and tell him that I'm determined to become a doctor and ask him if he will help me?"

"Not at all," Ruth had said. "Do it immediately—today, Jan. And if you tell him everything quite frankly, I'm sure the principal will help you with your work."

Right after that Jan regretted confiding in her—that was just like him—and before he left the room he threatened, "If you talk about it to anybody, you'll catch it!" That night Ruth was afraid to ask him what answer the principal had given him, but he came to her again and told her what had happened. The principal had said that Jan would have to prove through his work that he was sincere. "Without help, I won't make it anyway," Jan concluded dejectedly.

"How mean of the principal! . . ." Ruth was indignant. She couldn't sleep that night and the longer she thought about it, the angrier she became. She finally decided to go to the principal herself and ask if he would help Jan, so he wouldn't have to leave school. As she was afraid that maybe she wouldn't have the courage next morning (in the morning everything seemed so different, it was always like that), she promised herself that she would really do it. It would be cowardly not to and, therefore, she couldn't back out. If you promised something, even if it was only to yourself, you had to keep your promise.

Ruth waited till the school bell rang before she emerged from her hiding place, a doorway on the other side of the street. She pressed the bell near the large entrance door and trembling with fear waited for the janitor to open the door.

The janitor looked very much surprised. "Well, *Jongejuffrouw?*" he asked.

"May I . . . may I . . . speak to the principal?"

"Now? The principal is busy."

"It is very important," Ruth said as firmly as she could.

"The principal is in class now, but he will be free next hour. You'll have to wait fifty minutes, *Juffertje.*" He led her to the waiting-room. "Shouldn't you be in school yourself?" he asked as they walked down the long school corridor.

"No," Ruth lied.

She could hear the voices of the teachers and children coming from the class rooms. Suppose, she thought, that Jan or Jaap should be walking in the hall and see her! . . .

Waiting was the worst thing of all, Ruth thought, for while she was sitting there she found her venture more and more frightening and she wondered how she had ever dared to start on it. She stayed there alone till the bell had rung and the noise of the changing classes had died down.

The principal came to fetch her himself. "Well, well . . ." he said, and Ruth thought that he was laughing at her, because his eyes behind the glasses looked very much amused. "Well . . . well . . . and with whom do I have the honor? . . ."

"I am Ruth," she said, "and I have to ask you something."

"Oh, my," said the principal, "is it as serious as all that?"

"Yes," nodded Ruth. Again she walked through the long corridor, this time behind the principal, and then she was sitting opposite him at his desk.

"Let's see, Ruth, say, what a nice name, have you come to tell me that you want to enter the H.B.S.?"

"No," said Ruth, "I've come for my brother Jan."

"Which Jan?"

"Jan van Oordt."

"I see. . . ." said the principal abruptly. Yes, he was angry with Jan, Ruth could tell by his voice and his face, and therefore it was twice as hard to go on.

"I wanted . . . I thought . . ." said Ruth. A lump came into her throat, but she swallowed it courageously.

"I wanted to promise you," she said then, "that Jan will work hard, I mean, I'll see to it that he'll work hard, if you please won't send him to the M.U.L.O., for then he can't become a doctor, and he wants to so badly." She looked at the principal imploringly.

"Well . . . well . . ." The director walked around his desk and sat down on the edge. "Well . . . well, Ruth," he said, and suddenly Ruth thought he was really nice and she wasn't at all afraid any more. "That fellow Jan is certainly lucky to have such a sweet little sister. He doesn't deserve it."

"Oh yes, he does," nodded Ruth. "Jan is . . . I mean . . ." She didn't know very well what to say. "Jan can work very well. I will see to it," she said then.

"I wonder," said the principal. "Frankly, I doubt it. Don't you think that Jan had better go to the M.U.L.O. after all?"

"Oh, no," said Ruth heatedly. "Then he can't become a doctor, and it means so much to Vader. Please let Jan stay at school."

The principal sat down again behind his desk. "Jan has really been lazy. All the teachers are complaining about him. He only does half of his homework. He works hard only in the gym. I've lost my patience with him."

Ruth didn't know whether to get up now and leave. Hesitantly she slid to the edge of her chair.

The principal folded his fingertips one against the other and looked at them seriously. Then he said, "Well, all right then, I'll tell Jan what you have promised me; that you will see to it that he works hard. I'll give him an extra assignment every day, so that he can gradually catch up with the class. No soccer, no scouting, no skating. No playing except on Sunday afternoons. Can you see to that, Ruth? Do you really think you can?"

"Yes," Ruth nodded, her eyes shining. Suddenly she started. "Jan mustn't know that I was here," she said.

"Why not?"

"He'll be furious with me."

"I'll tell him that we are going to help him together," said the principal, "and I think he'll be very glad, Ruth."

He nodded reassuringly. Then he suddenly asked, "Aren't you supposed to be in school, Ruth?"

That question scared her very much and those embarrassing tears sprang to her eyes.

"How would you like a cup of chocolate?" The principal took a vacuum flask out of his desk and poured Ruth a cup. She swallowed the tears with the chocolate and when she had finished with it, she could look at him quietly.

"You go to the village school, don't you, Ruth? Shall I write a note to juffrouw Van Steenbergen?"

The principal took a slip of paper and wrote a note full of little letters, with his fountain pen.

A little later, Ruth was on the train, on her way to school at peace with herself, and with, oh, such a grateful feeling.

Chapter 5

JAAP

WHEN JAAP came into the living room at half past six in the morning to practice the piano as usual, he found Werner sitting in a chair near the lukewarm stove, huddled in a coat, with a book on his knees.

"What are you doing here so early?"

"Jan is already working and I didn't want to disturb him."

"Did Jan say that you disturbed him?"

"Oh, no."

While Jaap was opening the piano, he thought about Werner who, although he had been with them for almost two weeks, was as shy as ever, and always felt that he was a burden to them. The other children couldn't quite understand it, they were all so secure themselves, so used to their own little place in the world. Jaap felt that Werner's fear and shyness were the result of his horrible treatment in Germany. All the children were very nice to Werner and tried to draw him into all their activities, but at the same time they were at a loss as to how to handle the whole situation and with all their pity they still couldn't strike quite the right note. Jaap was very natural with him and for that reason Werner felt more at ease with Jaap.

"Am I disturbing you?" asked Werner.

"I'll forget about you while I'm playing, don't worry," said Jaap.

But he didn't forget. He was very conscious of the boy sitting behind him, and it distracted him more than Geesje's vacuum cleaning in the consulting-room. Maybe that was because Geesje didn't listen, and Werner did.

Jaap turned around. "Do you like music?"

"Oh, yes."

"Do you play the piano?"

"No, I played the violin."

"Say, then we can play together, sonatas and things."

Werner smiled faintly. "I haven't a violin."

"Maybe we can borrow one from somebody."

While Jaap played on he thought, imagine, being young like Werner, and having to leave everything behind, everything. Your violin, although that isn't even the worst thing. But your work, your school, like Werner, who had been in the Latin College. And even that was not the worst. The town where you lived. And then . . . your parents . . . terrible. You fled over the border, you didn't even have any papers, because it was safer to tear them up. There you were. You had a suit of clothes and a coat, shoes, stockings, a little underwear . . . your memories and your homesickness. That was all.

And Werner wasn't the only one. . . . There were thousands like him.

Jaap didn't bother with his scales and exercises, but took his worn Beethoven volume. He had to express that feeling in him, that fury over injustice . . .

Later, when the others came down for breakfast, Jaap took Jan aside. "That bed of Werner's can go in my room, if he bothers you."

"Who says he bothers me?" Jan flared. He had been very irritable lately. Immediately after his conversation with the principal Jan had been very happy, but later, when he had gotten the task, a large sheet of paper, divided into rectangles that were completely filled up with the fine handwriting of the principal, his spirits had suddenly dropped again. Jan wasn't used to working hard. He started in the morning at six o'clock, worked till half past seven, had breakfast, and took the train to school. After school, at noon, he had lunch with his friends in a cafeteria. That was the only time he could relax. At four o'clock he went straight home, worked till dinner time and after that, till ten o'clock. Yes, Jan was tired and consequently irritable. Poor Ruth, who had helped him so faithfully, had to pay for it. When, for instance, she met him after dinner in the upstairs hall where Jan was playing ball for a moment against the door of the linen closet, he would snap, "Yes, yes, I'm already on my way. Don't worry, I'm going to work."

But Ruth bore with it courageously, because she understood very well that all this working was a real ordeal for happy-go-lucky Jan; he was grateful to Ruth but he wouldn't let on, not for all the world. The family who didn't know anything of what had happened made remarks such as, Gosh, Jan, what zeal. . . . Does the spirit move you, Jan? . . . Better late than never. . . .

So Jan said, "Who says that Werner bothers me! . . . Did he say that?"

"Oh no, but I see that you're rather busy and that Werner is afraid of disturbing you."

"Yes, I'm very busy," said Jan. "I loafed a little, see," he continued a little embarrassed.

"My room is larger," said Jaap, "and I practice downstairs early in the morning anyway, so Werner can sleep longer. And in the afternoons when I have either piano lessons or I practice the organ in church, he'll have the place to himself."

So with Moeder's approval they changed Jaap's room; Jaap even built a complete corner for Werner, and emptied half of his clothes closet for him.

Werner was visibly picking up, and Moeder didn't have to keep finding things with which to keep him busy. He withdrew into his own little corner. He read the German and English books that Jaap got for him from the library, and studied hard in a Dutch grammar.

He also wrote long letters to his parents, but Jaap found them later in little pieces in the waste basket. When Jaap tactfully asked him about it, Werner admitted with his usual, somewhat bitter little smile, "It's better to be careful."

"Do they know then that you're safely here?"

"Yes," Werner said only and Jaap didn't ask any more.

A few days later Jaap came home with a violin, which he had borrowed from a friend at school. Ruth, who had seen him with the instrument under his arm, asked,

"And now are you going to learn to play the violin, Japie?"

"Miss Curiosity," answered Jaap.

But the next morning at half past six the family, who was still in bed, heard the tuning of the violin, and after that the strains of a Haydn sonata with piano accompaniment sounded through the house.

"Do you hear that?" Moeder asked Vader.

"Yes," said Vader and he saw that Moeder had tears in her eyes.

"How is Werner's uncle now?" she asked.

"Getting better, temperature normal. He'll probably be released from the hospital soon."

"And then what?" asked Moeder.

Vader, who had gotten up, sat down on the edge of her bed. "Listen, would you mind if Werner stayed with us for the time being?"

"Mind? . . ." Moeder asked indignantly.

"I mean, wouldn't it be too much for you?"

"It's too much as it is anyway, for Geesje and me. I must get some help, a girl for your practice who can also go out with Anne."

"Do you have somebody in mind?"

"When I go to town next week for the *Sinterklaas* shopping, I can go to the employment agency at the same time. But why is Werner going to stay with us?"

"I saw his uncle yesterday in the hospital. He has an affidavit for America, but the boy hasn't. The uncle can only see to Werner's papers when he has arrived in America."

"Until then Werner will stay with us!"

As Moeder dressed the baby, she listened. When she came down she found Ruth on the floor near the piano, Pieter Pim standing on the other side. Even Jan had left his books. Werner was playing with flushed cheeks.

"Beautiful, isn't it?" whispered Gees, who was quietly setting the breakfast table.

When Werner noticed that they were all standing around him, he suddenly broke off his playing and fled from the room. He stayed away from breakfast, and the children, on their way to school, saw him in the car with Vader, driving across the heath.

Later in the kitchen, Gees said to Moeder, "The boy has been crying terribly, *Mevrouw*. Doctor took him with him to divert him a little. Sad, isn't it?"

Moeder sat down at the kitchen table. "Horrible, Gees. When I think that one of my children . . ."

"Did you hear the radio last night? All furloughs have been cancelled. There are rumors again about an invasion. You don't know what to think any more."

"They call that a war of nerves, Gees."

"Then they're certainly succeeding with me," said Gees jokingly. "It's making me awfully nervous. Do you think that they're going to build shelters in the village too? The notary has one already, and there are two of them in the baron's garden. But who is taking care of the other people?"

"There are already several shelters in town, Gees."

"But not in the village, Mevrouw, and it's high time they did something about it. They're always talking about gas masks, but the shelters certainly are much more important."

"Just imagine," Moeder suddenly said, "just imagine if there were really an invasion."

"Oh, but no," Gees tried to reassure her, "those are just rumors, politics, Mevrouw. They didn't come in the last war, and they won't come now."

"Imagine, Gees, if I couldn't get enough milk for Anne," Moeder continued.

"Don't worry now, Mevrouw. They won't take Antje's milk away from her. I'm still here!"

Moeder laughed, but deep inside she didn't feel easy. She went to the living room to listen to the news broadcast. . . .

Some days later Jaap came to his father. "In the paper it says that there is a committee for Jewish refugees. Will we help too?"

"I haven't heard anything about it in the village yet," Vader told him.

"I would like to give a concert in the church for the benefit of the Jewish refugees."

"How would you go about it, Jaap?"

"Well, Vader, I'd like you to discuss it in the church council. Then on one of the Sundays before Christmas Mr. Van der Wiel, the minister, would have to preach about the persecution of the Jews, and I would play a few pieces and finally there would be a collection."

"Do you think Mr. Van der Wiel will be willing?"

"He often talks about these things in catechism class, Vader."

"Do you think that you're good enough at the organ?"

Jaap smiled. "You haven't heard me for quite some time, Vader. I've done rather well. Couldn't you come and listen, this afternoon while I'm practicing?"

"I could manage. We could go to Mr. Van der Wiel together after that and talk about your plan.

"At half past five then, Vader."

That afternoon the doctor was sitting in his own pew in the little village church, listening to the organ. In the empty church the organ sounded abnormally loud, but the doctor enjoyed it.

On Sunday mornings, at the service, the organist played the old hymns very slowly, but even his tempo appeared to be too fast for the villagers, who were always singing half a beat behind the organ. Jaap played differently. He really drew music from the primitive instrument, and the doctor listened attentively.

"You're improved tremendously, Jaap," he praised him later. "Do you prefer the organ to the piano?"

"I don't know yet, Vader. In a year or so I'll decide. The piano has more concert possibilities, but the organ . . . I don't know."

Mr. Van der Wiel was very pleased.

"How did you hit on that idea, Jaap?" he asked.

"Because of the boy we have at home. He's exactly like Jan and me and all the others. It's such an injustice, such . . . such . . ." Jaap who never could express himself very well, where it concerned emotion, spread his hands and shrugged his shoulders. "I guess you understand," he concluded.

And so they decided on the date of the performance. If the church council consented, Jaap's concert would take place on the Sunday before Christmas.

Chapter 6

PIETER PIM

It was six o'clock in the morning when Pieter Pim woke up. That's that, we're through with that again, he sighed. Pieter thought that sleeping was a waste of time, and if Vader hadn't thought it best for his health, Pieter would surely never have gone to bed at all. Now he would have to stay in bed for hours and hours yet, until it was time to get up. In summer, at least, you could do all kinds of things in bed, but in winter it was pitch dark and as for turning the light on . . . it wasn't allowed. He couldn't even do that. Why were all those beautiful pictures on the wall—pictures of planes, Diesel trains just like the ones that ran to Amsterdam, and other fast things—if you couldn't see them? . . . No, Pieter wasn't very pleased with life, as mothers arranged it for boys. They should really let you go your own way. Then, at least, things happened to you. Do you think it was possible for an ordinary boy with a clean shirt, and hands you had to wash forever (not to mention nails to clean, hair to comb and more of that sort of thing), a boy who always had to ask first if he could go to the village, and who had to come home on time, a boy who wasn't allowed to get up before seven, I ask you, do you think it was possible for a boy like that to have real adventures? . . . You bet your life not. Could you ever do something tremendous that way?

While Pieter Pim lay waiting in his bed in the morning from six till seven, he sometimes thought such nice things. You know, things, that could very well happen some day, if only you got the chance. Like rescuing a child from the water, just like that, one-two-three-go-after-it.

Or save a child from a burning house for example. Then you got a medal from *Koningin* Wilhelmina. With that jumping-in-the-pond business you got one also.

Those were the kinds of things Pieter Pim thought about when he woke up in the morning and then the waiting didn't seem so long.

Today he would make the rounds with Uienkruier, the greengrocer who was a friend of Pieter Pim's. Hein Uienkruier was a marvelous fellow. You could tell that even from his name, which means onioncarrier. A fellow whose name is Hein Uienkruier and who is a greengrocer, is a fine fellow, all right.

He had a fine horse too. It was called Gezina, and there wasn't a better horse in the whole wide world. Even Hein said that.

Pieter Pim was very often allowed to go with him on the cart, and visit the customers. That was in summertime, you see. In winter it was too cold, Moeder thought, but now Moeder was very busy, and people who are busy shouldn't be bothered with questions. That's why Pieter didn't ask her. And it was really high time that he went along with Hein, else he would think that Pieter didn't like it any more, and when it was summer, he would be left to twiddle his thumbs.

"Pieter Pim, will you put on your scarf and your ice-cap when you go to play outside?" Moeder called from the bedroom, when Pieter was going down to eat his breakfast. "Vader says it's bitter cold."

Hein Uienkruier was already back from the auction in town. How cold he looked! Pieter almost had to laugh at Hein's nose, which was the color of his best red cabbage.

"I wish I were your father," said Hein when they filled up the cart together. "He's sitting nice and warm in his car and is invited in by every customer and even gets hot coffee from them. I have to stay outside the door everywhere. I don't see why you want to come along today, Pieter, for it's darned cold on top of the cart."

Pieter did think it a bit funny that Hein talked about his father's "customers." They were his "patients," but otherwise Hein was right. And then his father even wore a fur-lined jacket, and it had a fur collar too. No, things weren't divided fairly in this world. Even Pieter Pim's father said so himself sometimes. Therefore he would think it quite all right if . . .

"Will you wait for me, Hein?" Pieter asked all of a sudden. "I have to go home for a moment, but I'll be back soon."

Pieter took good care that Geesje didn't see him taking Vader's jacket from the coat rack. Gees sometimes made a fuss about the most ordinary things. With the jacket over his arm Pieter Pim returned to Hein.

"Here you are, from Vader," he said, very pleased with his idea.

"Well, well," said Hein, "you see, there are still some decent people in the world; I must say, Pieter, that your father hurt me badly the other day when I had that festering finger, but this, Pieter, this . . ."

Hein was moved by it all, and Pieter thought it so embarrassing that he quickly straightened a basket of sprouts on the other side of the cart. Everything in its right place!

At last they were off. Goodness, was it cold!

Pieter Pim had to sit down on his hands, else they were sure to get frozen, and as for his feet . . . better not talk about them. Still it was lovely. Especially because Hein felt so nice and warm. He sat drawing at his pipe like a king and asserting for the twenty-sixth time that he felt much less cold than usual, and that there were still decent people in the world who didn't begrudge things to their fellow men.

The people on the road stopped to look at Hein Uienkruier. He was a good-looking fellow all right, but he was not so handsome that a man should stop to stare at him in all that cold. To tell the truth it was a little funny, that business with the fur jacket. The coat fitted all right, but did you ever see a greengrocer wearing a light grey jacket with a fur collar around his neck? Of course you have, on Sundays, at church, but on a greengrocer's cart? . . . Never! It looks like a flag on a broomstick. . . . Wait, wait, don't compare Hein with a broomstick. That's unkind, but still . . . don't forget that that same morning he had been weighing dusty potatoes, that he had washed beets, and that the last time he had shaved was on Sunday. But Hein was tremendously pleased with himself, and Pieter was also tremendously pleased with him. They called on all the customers. Pieter Pim climbed off the cart thirty times and rang the bells and shouted in a real greengrocer's voice "Uienkruier . . ." deep down in his throat, drawing-out each syllable. He helped weigh the potatoes and cabbage and carrots. He assorted chicory and kale, for he could distinguish those two, even when they weren't cooked and not everybody can do that. He was as busy as a bee.

While they were driving along Pieter saw a car approaching which could very well have been his father's car. And it really *was*. You could recognize it immediately because it was better than any other car, at least that's what Pieter thought.

From his seat he could see his father and he also saw that he looked angry, terribly angry. He stopped right next to Gezina, so nothing on the road could pass.

And yet Vader knew his traffic rules really well. He jumped out of the car, slammed the door angrily behind him, and came straight up to Hein.

Pieter got a funny feeling in the pit of his stomach, that didn't improve when he noticed that his Vader was wearing his summer coat and looked very chilly, with his shoulders hunched up and his hands deep in his coat pockets. Maybe it hadn't been Vader's intention after all to share everything with his fellow men. He didn't begrudge Hein much, but maybe with his only winter coat it was different. Pieter Pim began to doubt.

"Well, Uienkruier, you certainly take things for granted," said Vader pulling down the right corner of his mouth in a certain way.

At first Hein didn't say anything at all and when he did say something it wasn't anything special. "Look, doctor . . . I thought . . . Pieter said . . . you mustn't think . . . it isn't my habit . . ."

"You can't tell me, Uienkruier, that you believed that child. You saw very well that it was my fur jacket. I don't like that kind of thing, my friend."

Then Uienkruier became angry too. "Now see here, doctor, I won't let you insult me; if you think I stole that coat . . ."

"Now, now," the doctor said.

"Now, now, nothing!" shouted Uiengruier, a little louder than the doctor. "The child brings me the coat and says 'from Vader.' Well, what do I think then? That you surely have some other ones and that this is an old one you can spare."

Vader looked a bit dejected because Uienkruier mistook his beautiful jacket for an old one. Apparently he had thought so before, because he had wiped his hands clean on it after he had weighed the sauerkraut.

Pieter didn't feel very much at ease. Vader didn't look at all in his direction, and that meant he was saving all his attention for later. Moreover on either side of them cars and cyclists that couldn't pass were piling up, people were gathering around them and . . . "Of all things," thought Pieter Pim, the village constable was making his way through the crowd with real constable-gestures of his arms.

"Well, doctor, what's wrong! A collision?" he asked.

Pieter immediately saw himself sitting in prison with Hein Uienkruier, as plain as day. . . . What would Jan say when he heard of it? Then he thought of all the scary things you heard about prisons, and his heart started to thump everywhere except in the spot where it really was.

"My son," said Vader, "has lent my winter jacket to Uienkruier here, and we are deciding what we should do. I would certainly like to have my jacket back, for it's cold in the car, but we can't swap, for Uienkruier can't sit on the cart with only my summer coat on."

"Yeah . . ." said the constable and he thoughtfully stroked his chin with a big constable's thumb. "That's a difficult case, doctor, but first you'll have to clear the road."

Pieter Pim thought that he was mistaken when he saw a twinkle in the constable's eyes, and that he had seen his father wink was surely a mistake, too.

"You know what, Uienkruier," said the doctor, "just

put your cart around the corner, and Pieter Pim will take care of it, while we go in my car to get your coat."

And that's what happened. Pieter was allowed to take care of the cart all by himself, which is important on a road full of children on their way home from school.

When Uienkruier returned and they were driving back to Pieter's home—it was lunch-time already and besides, Hein had to sell Geesje some vegetables—Uienkruier said, "All the same, Pieter, your father is an extraordinary man, and he has compassion for his fellow men. He did hurt me very much the other day, with that festering finger, but still, Pieter . . . a noble man! . . ."

Pieter Pim sat on his cold hands and pretended that he wasn't at all proud of his father.

That same afternoon Pieter was standing with Ruth's skates on the skating rink but he forgot to skate, everything was so gay and beautiful around him. The flags were flying in the wind (it was cold all right), the music was real skating music, and the people laughed and talked and had lots of fun. It was a good thing that Pieter stayed on the side, for the big boys who could skate well flew round the curves like express trains. The girls in gay sweaters were skating in twosomes, with crossed hands, or gliding, giggling and shouting, in long rows over the pond. The older people were skimming step-over-step on figure skates. Well, Pieter didn't see much in that. You didn't make much headway, because you skated in little curves all the time. No, on Frisian skates, that was much more real, with your head bent against the wind, and with your hands on your back. He would also like to be an ice-sweeper. Then you could skate the whole day, on top of which you made money, too.

Pieter tightened his lips and started to move slowly in the direction of the "little scramblers' rink" for children, who were learning. That was a roped off area in the center of the rink. Very carefully, foot by foot, Pieter Pim scrambled in the direction of his goal, and when he finally arrived he didn't know which was hurting him more, his feet or his back side. He sat down on a little bench.

"You don't know how to skate, do you?" said a boy, who was sitting next to him.

"Oh, I can skate very well. I just pretend I can't," Pieter said proudly.

"I don't like it at all; I'm so cold," said the boy in a tearful voice. Pieter looked very closely at him and then he saw that the boy wasn't at all a skating-boy. He had put on exactly as many clothes as his mother had told him: an ice-cap, a scarf, gloves, and at least three sweaters. A real mother's boy, Pieter thought.

"What's your name?" he asked.

"Pieter," said the boy. "What's yours?"

"Also Pieter, Pieter Pim."

"Will you be my friend?" asked the boy.

Pieter Pim seriously thought this over. "I can't," he then said.

"Why not?"

"Because we have the same name."

"At school they call me Pieter Pimple," said the boy and pointed to a wart over his right eye.

Pieter came a little nearer. Gosh, a boy who went to school already and who asked him to be his friend. That was a tremendous honor, yessir!

"I got ten cents from my mother. Let's go and have some anise-milk," said Pieter Pimple.

In a jiffy Pieter Pim had taken off his skates. Anise-milk! You bet your life he liked that!

At the end of the rink a row of little *koek* booths had been put up, where you would buy all sorts of things. Pea soup with pork-knuckles, and chocolate milk, and raisin-rolls and almond cake, and a lot of other lovely things. You could also have your skates ground there.

Pieter Pimple ordered two cups of anise-milk from the fat lady with all the heavy clothes on, who was telling, in a voice like a trumpet, how very good her anise-milk was and how thickly she spread the butter on her raisin-rolls. Inches thick, folks! While Pieter was blowing on his hot milk, he watched the boys and girls, who were standing near the booths, talking, and laughing, and eating.

How about a raisin-roll?" asked Pieter Pimple.

Pieter Pim just nodded yes. What a marvelous friend he had picked up! While he was enjoying his raisin-roll, Pieter was thinking about what he would give the boy with the ten cents for which he would ask Moeder tomorrow. Chocolate milk and an almond cake. It was so grown-up to have a personal friend. Pieter's friends were all much older, Hein Uienkruier and Gezina, and Gees, but he had never had a real friend before. He lived outside the village and there were no children of his age nearby.

Pieter was startled from his dreams by the voice of the fat *juffrouw* in the booth. "Ten cents, young man." There you are, she called him "young man." So you see, if you had a friend who bought sweets for you, they called you "young man" straight away.

"He has the money," said Pieter and pointed at Pieter Pimple.

The juffrouw extended a large hand in a red mitten to Pieter Pimple, but that gentleman said, "I paid already, juffrouw."

"What about that boy?" she asked.

"He must pay for himself," said Pieter Pimple. "I haven't got any money left."

The juffrouw looked at Peter Pim very angrily and she said, "Give me your money, kid."

Yes, she called him "kid." No more "young man!"

"I have no money," said Pieter Pim in a small voice.

"Listen to that! First he drinks and eats, and then no money. You'll have to do better than that, if you want to make a fool of me."

"What's the matter," asked the man who was rinsing cups in the back of the booth.

"Same as usual," said the fat lady, "no money . . ."

"Come here, little fellow! You'll have to work for it."

And so, a short while later, Pieter Pim stood in front of the booth and shouted at the top of his voice how delicious the anise-milk was and how thickly the butter was spread on the raisin-rolls. Inches thick!

Pieter Pim didn't mind at all. Had he ever *earned* a cup of anise-milk and a raisin-roll before? He certainly hadn't!

Pieter Pimple, that good-for-nothing, stood staring at him, with his mouth wide open. And Pieter Pim yelled, "Anise-milk! . . . The best, the finest . . . Try our raisin-rolls with butter! . . ." just as he had heard it from the juffrouw.

After a while his voice failed him. Not that he wasn't willing any more, but his voice was just like a cracked trumpet.

When he decided to tell the juffrouw, that he had yelled long enough for one cup of anise-milk and a raisin-roll, but that if need be, he would go on for a little while, if she would give him a cup of chocolate milk, he saw his Vader approach. Vader with skates on and pulling Pieter's little sleigh. Imagine, Vader on the ice, just like that, on an ordinary weekday.

Well, at first Pieter Pim pretended of course that he didn't see Vader, and walking to and fro with large steps in front of the booth, he shouted as loudly as he could, "That delicious anise-milk, folks . . . and fresh raisin-rolls . . . and we put on the butter that thick . . . inches thick . . . delicious!"

Vader suddenly recognized Pieter's voice. You should have seen him look! It made Pieter feel hot all over. Vader pushed through the crowd and stared at him with his mouth open, just like Pieter Pimple. And did he laugh, then! Vader almost lost his balance laughing. But later, while he was pulling Pieter home on the sleigh, he said that he thought that Pieter was just like a real town-crier and that he could shout just as hard as the men in the market in Arnhem. . . . Yessir!

Chapter 7

A LETTER FROM MIEP

ONE EVENING, in the last week of November, Moeder announced that the next day she wouldn't be home for lunch—nor for tea.

"Gosh . . ." said Ruth, disappointed, "how dull, Moekie."

"Where are you going?" asked Pieter Pim.

"To town."

"May I come with you?"

"No, not this time."

"May my little sister come?" Pieter always called Anne "my little sister."

"Oh no, what an idea! Anne has to sleep."

"What are you going to do in town?"

"Well, I don't know if I ought to tell you," Moeder said mysteriously.

Vader gave Moeder a wink. "You can tell him all right, I think. Moeder is going to see if *Sinterklaas* has arrived yet from Spain."

"Oh heavens," Ruth, startled, put her hand to her mouth. "I forgot to make a wishing-list."

"No wishing-lists this year, mind you! This year we'll celebrate a very modest Sinterklaas. You're only going to get useful presents, and candy."

"How do you know, Moeder?" asked Pieter, puzzled.

"That's just what I'm going to tell Sinterklaas."

The older children were laughing among themselves. They really had fun because Moeder had made that slip. Pieter still believed in Sinterklaas.

"But I think that's really silly of you, Moeder," he said then, with great indignation. "Suppose that Sinterklaas wants to give me a pair of skates . . ."

"I think that skates are a very useful present for Pieter," said Vader. "A Dutch boy, five years old, should really be able to skate."

"I can do it, almost," said Pieter, triumphantly.

"Without falling?" asked Ruth.

"I can do ten strokes without falling," said Pieter Pim, and he looked at them so defiantly that nobody dared to laugh.

"That's good," said Vader. "You can ask for a pair of skates for Pieter, Moeder."

"With yellow straps," said Pieter.

"I'll write it down," promised Moeder. "Now run along and play a little, before you go to bed."

"I'm going to get my shoe ready," said Pieter.

"Yes, do." Vader threw a warning glance at the children, who were giggling. "Do you have any hay for Sinterklaas' horse?"

"Of course," said Pieter, "I got it from Hein Uienkruier."

When Pieter had left, Jan asked, "Why will we only get useful presents?"

"Don't you know there's a war going on?" Jaap asked with sarcasm.

"Well . . . what of it? What has that got to do with Sinterklaas?"

"First of all, I really don't think it's necessary for you to have an elaborate Sinterklaas, while there's so much sorrow and want in the world, Jan. And besides," Vader went on, "besides I would rather give my money to the victims of war. Think of the children in Czechoslovakia and Poland. You read the paper, don't you, Jan?"

"There'll be enough parcels," Moeder promised, "and you'll see what fun we'll have."

Jan shrugged his shoulders in embarrassment. "I didn't mean it that way. It's all right with me not to have any presents at all."

"Me too," Ruth added.

"I don't need anything," said Werner.

"Nonsense," said Moeder, "we'll give each other little things and a lot of funny 'surprises' with rhymes. If I were you, I would start making parcels now. And I want to say something. This year I intended to tell Pieter that Sinterklaas doesn't exist, but now that he still believes in it so firmly, I wouldn't like to spoil it for him. Shall we have Sinterklaas visit us once more?"

"Yes . . . oh, good . . ." They were all shouting at the same time, and then, like conspirators, they bent together over the table.

"Who will it be?"

"Jaap," proposed Ruth.

"No," said Jaap. "Last year Pieter almost recognized me. He looked at my mask in such a funny way, I almost couldn't help laughing."

"You couldn't anyway," said Jan. "You bit your beard every time you spoke."

"And when Vader had to sing a song for you, you turned around." Ruth screamed with laughter.

"Let's ask *Oom* Jan," Jaap proposed.

"He has been mobilized," said Vader.

"*Tante* Eef," suggested Moeder.

"Oh Moekie, she's much too fat. Just imagine! . . ."

At that moment Pieter came in with a letter. "From Miep," he said.

"How do you know that?" asked Moeder, surprised.

"I can smell it," said Pieter and held the letter to his nose.

"Let me smell," Ruth tried to snatch the letter from his hands, but Pieter Pim crawled under the table to Vader.

"The letter really smells of lavender," laughed Vader, who had examined it.

"Pieter Pim, you're a strange little fellow," Jan said, shaking his head. "Smelling a letter, indeed! . . ."

"When I go to school next year, I'll learn to read, and then I won't have to smell Miep's letters any more."

"Quiet, everybody," Vader ordered. "I'll read the letter."

MY DEAR EVERYBODY [wrote Miep],

I have been back in Amsterdam for ten days now, but I couldn't possibly write sooner. You've no idea of the amount of work I had to catch up with. And, to be honest, I've gone out a lot. Two concerts on my subscription, and once I went to the Popular Concert and I also saw a play.

It was about a violinist who later became a boxer, translated, of course, from the American. The subject was really a little strange for us Dutchmen, but it was acted beautifully. I can't imagine there's more art to be enjoyed anywhere in the world than in Amsterdam. All that music and so many plays, and the museums! Did you read that all the pictures in the Rijksmuseum have been put away for the duration and that there's going to be an exhibition of living Dutch painters, the largest ever? I'm very curious about it, although it will be rather strange to miss all those beautiful paintings of Rembrandt, Frans Hals, and Vermeer. Imagine the Rijksmuseum without the Night Watch! It's a good thing that Jan and Jaap came to Amsterdam with the school last year. Now they have at least seen all that old Dutch art. Who knows how long the war will last? Are they talking so much in the village about a possible invasion by the Germans? A week ago the news was threatening again. They're building shelters everywhere here. Even underneath the bridges over the canals. The world certainly is in a sad state. We're forced to misuse our lovely little old bridges to protect ourselves against our fellow men. When I talk like that at school, they laugh at me. Probably there's no room any more for idealists like your little Miep. Don't think that I'm escaping the truth—maybe I see the seriousness of the situation better than others. Vader, have you talked about shelters yet in the Village Council? It's high time that they see to the protection of the villagers. Here in town unemployed men, armed with big paint cans have painted the curbstones white in case of a blackout. You can understand what a tremendous job that was, but now the whole town is covered with a coat of snow, so that effort was all for nothing. What a waste of money and time. I'm glad that I'm not a member of the city council. I wouldn't care for it, not even in such a little village as ours.

You'll have a hard nut to crack with the farmers, won't you, Vader, when you start about the shelters? Holland hasn't waged a war in a hundred years. War is as remote to the Dutch as those years are long. Even with all those precautionary measures for "maintaining neutrality," as the diplomats put it, and now that the Water-linie has been flooded and you meet soldiers everywhere, even now, Amsterdam with all the canals under the snow still looks so peaceful. Last Sunday that tranquility struck me forcibly again. We made an excursion on skates, a real old-fashioned excursion to Gouda, first in my friend Maarten's car and then further on skates. It was beautiful. A bright blue sky, and all the ditches and canals shone like mirrors under the sun. Most of the ice was wonderful and lots of people took advantage of it. Whole families holding on to one long pole passed us by, in the center the smaller children, who sometimes just let themselves be pulled along because they were tired. Next year we should definitely make a trip like that sometime, all of us! On one pole! In Gouda, Maarten bought a long Gouda pipe, and for me a box with real "sprits," Gouda cookies. We were home before dark, dead tired, of course, but nevertheless we went to the popular concert in the *Concertgebouw*.

Now it's almost Sinterklaas again. Oh dears, how I'm looking forward to it! It is true that people say that in these times it isn't fitting to celebrate Sinterklaas, but it seems as though everybody is doing twice as much shopping as in other years. On December 5th we'll celebrate

Sinterklaas at school, and after that I'm going "home." Hurrah!

The rest of the letter is for the older children, and of course for Vader and Moeder. Pieter Pim must leave the room for a moment, it's a surprise for him.——

Protesting violently, Pieter Pim left the room, but not before Moeder had promised that she would bring him a cookie in bed. Vader continued,

—This year they're going to stage a great entry of Sinterklaas. It is really meant as a lesson to the shopkeepers, who "use" Sinterklaas for advertising purposes and so hurt the children's belief and confidence in the good Saint. You sometimes see three or four Sinterklazen here in the same street. They drive past each other in cars and greet each other and have great fun. It has even happened that two hired Sinterklazen had a drop too much and were sprawling in the street, locked in a furious fight. To check these things several people have formed a committee to restore the old custom of the big reception. One of our well-known actors will represent Sinterklaas. He will arrive on a boat and will get off at the Saint Nicolaas church. There his white horse will be waiting for him. Preceded by Moors, carrying baskets of oranges, and surrounded by Spanish noblemen, represented by Amsterdam students, he will ride to the Town Hall, where the mayor will receive him.

It's a pity that I won't be able to see it, but I'm going to bring our own Sinterklaas along! . . . Don't look so surprised. My friend Maarten whom I have wanted you to meet for a long time, will come and act as the good bishop.

The last part of the letter is only for Vader and Moeder.

"Pooh," said Ruth, "I know what's in it anyhow."

"What?" asked Jan surprised.

"She's going to marry Maarten, of course."

"You're crazy!" said Jan, but Vader who was finishing the letter for himself, threw a quick glance at Moeder. She came to read the letter with him, over his shoulder. But beg as she did later on, Ruth didn't get to hear the secret.

After the children had gone to bed, Vader and Moeder talked seriously to each other. Vader raised his cup of tea and said gaily, "To the happiness of your eldest daughter, Moeder."

Chapter 8

SINTERKLAAS

"THERE'S 'THE LEVEL LAND,'" Miep pointed out, when, in the late afternoon of the fifth of December they came driving over the heath in Maarten's rambling old Ford.

"Let me take a good look at it," he said, and stopped the car. "So there's where you were born, Miep. And now I can visualize what you told me. That's where you lay in the baby carriage in the sun, and a year later they put your play pen on the little lawn and all your vader's patients came to say 'hello' to you before they entered. And another year later you walked around the house with your hoop, and you played with your top on the brick path, and you drove your doll carriage carefully over the little lane with the rose bushes on either side."

They both looked in silence at the low, old-fashioned house, that was gazing over the heath with its window-eyes. The lights burned in all the rooms, in Ruth's room behind the gay little curtains, in the rooms of Jan and Jaap behind the carelessly drawn net curtains, and in the living room, where Moeder's plants on the window sill cast fantastic shadows against the window.

Beyond, the tree tops of a fir-forest drew a bluish line in the darkening evening. A peasant's cart drove over the heath-path, the thud of the horse's shoes sounding clearly in the silence. In the distance the whistle of the little steam train blew shrilly.

"What stillness!" said Maarten. "No wonder you're so attached to your house. I don't see how you can stand the noise in Amsterdam."

"I'll come back here soon," said Miep, "with you."

"I hope so," said Maarten.

"Do you think that the war will last long, Maarten?"

He started the motor. "I'm afraid it will."

"At home they think that we will stay out of it," said Miep hesitantly.

"There are many such naïve people."

"They rely on our neutrality."

Maarten shrugged his shoulders. "We're just like the little boy," he said then, "the little boy who said that he could go to school all alone, but who, once past the corner grasped the hand of his older brother. We can all do it so well alone . . ." he concluded bitterly, "all the small nations."

"Well, we, in our generation know at least how it shouldn't be," said Miep, "anyway, that's what we think."

"We know indeed, you and I, and later your brothers and sisters will know. There are hundreds and thousands like us in the world. Those are the people who after this war, will point the way to those who did not have that understanding, who never learned the truth, the truth that we are, all of us, members of one gigantic family."

"That is if we get the chance to point that way," said Miep.

"We must *take* that chance."

Maarten stopped in front of the gate and immediately faces appeared in the windows, and in the doorway. Ruth's curious little face, Pieter Pim, a little shy, and Moeder, beaming with joy that now they would all be together on Sinterklaas evening.

Kees ran out of the house, barking, and jumped, delirious with joy, up at Miep.

"Better leave the Sinterklaas mask and beard in the car. You'll change in the laboratory anyway. Pieter Pim is a bright little boy. . . ." Miep advised.

"Welcome," Moeder said to Maarten, and "Welcome, my boy," said Vader in the doorway of the living room.

When they were all seated 'round the table, drinking

tea, Ruth could no longer suppress her curiosity. "Are you going to marry him, Miep?" she asked confidentially, but loud enough to be heard by everybody.

"If you don't mind," Maarten said.

That silenced Ruth, but the others burst out laughing.

Miep looked a little uncertainly at Vader and Moeder. but they nodded encouragingly at her and then, to Ruth's great amazement, Miep came and hugged them.

"I thought that it was done quite differently," Ruth said, disappointed. "I thought that he had to come and ask for her hand, with a top hat on and a funny coat with flaps."

"That will happen," promised Maarten, "as soon as I've finished my studies." Ruth looked at him sideways. She really didn't know what to make of him.

"What are you studying?" Jaap asked.

"History."

"Come, children," Moeder said, "I'm sure you haven't even half finished making your parcels. We'll eat early and start immediately after dinner."

They ran for the door, for it was true that they weren't ready.

Ruth, particularly, was very busy. She had to make the parcels for Jan, too. At first they had quarreled. The parcels were completed with continuous squabblings, alternated, of course, with fits of laughter when they were preparing the "surprises."

For Ruth didn't want Jan to spend time wrapping

his presents. She tried to keep him at his daily task, as she had done ever since she had visited the principal.

"I promised the principal, that you would make it," Ruth complained. "And when I want to keep you at your work, you get mad. I know that it's a bore, but I would like so much for you to go to the second grade. I really don't know what to say any more."

"But you can see that I'm working hard. I really don't do anything else. Even when we had an ice-vacation last week, I worked the whole day. But you just keep nagging, like an old school marm."

Then Jan felt sorry for her. "You know very well that it was marvelous of you to go and see him. But you must understand that that nagging of yours is driving me crazy. You're so much younger than I am."

"But I do a lot of things for you. I listen to your lessons, and I copy your notes."

"Now don't fuss, you're O.K. Did you lock the door? Pieter keeps trying to get in. You must put Moeder's present at the bottom of a jar of starch."

"Oh, no," it made Ruth shiver. "Does Moekie have to mess around in starch? How gruesome."

"Just do it. Here's a jar. I swiped it especially for this in the chemistry room. Ask Gees if you can make some starch. Take care that you don't break the jar." Jan bent over his work again and Ruth went to the kitchen to prepare the "surprise" for Moeder. In the upstairs hall Pieter Pim was walking up and down. He tried to peek into Jaap's room, but Jaap locked his door and yelled to Pieter to go away. Pieter didn't really understand. Did you get your presents from Sinterklaas or from people? He racked his brain. How could Black Pete creep down through the chimney? He had really done it, because four times already Pieter Pim had found something in his shoe under the chimney, and the hay he had put in his shoe himself had gone. He had also put out the shoe for his little sister. That is, for want of a shoe, he had put down one of her little socks, and the next morning there had been two pink ribbons in it.

"You better go down to the living room," advised Ruth. "It's so cold here in the hall. Maybe Sinterklaas is going to strew candies before he comes."

But the door of the living room was also locked, so Pieter went to the kitchen for comfort.

"You come as if I had sent for you," Gees said. "Here, stick that lemon full of cloves. That's just the job for you. When it's ready, it'll look just like a porcupine. Wait and see."

"What's it for, Gees?"

"For the wine punch, for the grown-up people. You're going to get hot chocolate." Gees started to stir the pot of pea soup. She was grumbling at Ruth, who wanted to boil starch. "What a to-do there is in the house! The bell didn't stop ringing for a moment during the whole day."

"All parcels, Gees?" Ruth asked excitedly.

"Doesn't Sinterklaas bring the parcels himself?" Pieter Pim inquired. Now he would find out what it was all about.

"Do you think that old man can carry all those parcels himself?"

"And what about Black Pete?"

"He has his hands full, my boy. He has to look through the chimney to see if the children have been good. He has a list . . . this long . . . " Gees spread her arms out wide. . . . "It has the names of all children; the ones who have been good get a little dash, the ones who have been naughty, a little cross. Those with the cross get a birch whip and if they have been very naughty, *Pieterbaas* takes them along in his bag to Spain. But don't you be scared," she continued. "You'll get a little dash, for you're a good boy."

Yet Pieter Pim looked a little anxiously at the chimney above the large, square kitchen stove. "I haven't done anything naughty," he said then, "only by mistake."

"That's right. Hurry up with that porcupine. We'll eat right away."

At that moment the kitchen door was opened a crack and somebody strewed handfuls of candy into the kitchen, little sweets, and gingerbread-nuts and chocolates. Pieter left his porcupine and Ruth left her little pan with starch and they started to scramble for all they were worth.

"Well, what do you know, and in the kitchen, too," said Gees. "I'm sure that Black Pete heard what I said. He has his eyes and ears everywhere. He must have been on the roof just then."

Pieter stopped grabbing. "It came through the kitchen door," he said.

"No," said Gees. "Through the chimney, I got a gingerbread nut on my head."

"I saw the kitchen door being opened," Pieter maintained.

"That was the wind, but the strewing came from the chimney."

"I saw it too," said Ruth.

Pieter sat in the center of the kitchen floor and looked doubtfully from one to the other. "I wouldn't fib if I were you, Gees," he warned seriously. "If Sint hears you, he'll take you along to Spain."

"Then I'd better start packing my suitcase," said Gees with a wink at Ruth. "Come, Jan Stavast, pick that stuff up quickly, else I'll step on it. A good thing that I just scrubbed the floor! Here, put it in this box. You'll surely get some more candy later on."

The meal was over very quickly. The children were excited, ate as fast as they could, and disappeared again immediately to put the last touch to their parcels.

There was excited whispering and giggling behind doors, on stairs and in hallways. Jaap, Werner, and Ruth ran up and down the stairs, Vader had locked himself in his consulting-room, while Moeder and Gees prepared the living room for the great event. Jan, Miep, and Maarten had suddenly disappeared. Only Pieter Pim was sitting in a corner by the window, looking from the chimney to the door and from the door to the chimney.

He had a heavy feeling in his legs, and his stomach was almost in his throat.

"Put the chair for Sinterklaas there, Gees," he heard Moeder say, and he saw Gees put the big armchair in the middle of the room. The table had been pushed aside and a number of chairs were placed in a semi-circle.

"Moeder," Pieter asked, "Moeder, do you think that Sinterklaas himself is coming again?"

"I invited him," said Moeder.

"He's almost here already," said Gees. "He even let Black Pete strew, didn't he?"

Pieter looked out of the window. Maybe he would see Sinterklaas ride over the roof of the farm nearby. "You might as well start singing a song," Moeder advised. "The Sint will hear it if he is near."

Pieter stood under the chimney, and sang, as hoarse as a hen, with the excitement.

Zie ginds komt de stoomboot
Uit Spanje al aan.
Hij brengt ons Sint Nicolaas,
Ik zie hem al staan.

Zijn knecht staat te lachen
En wenkt ons reeds toe.
Wie zoet is, krijgt lekkers,
Wie stout is een roe.

Pieter Pim sang several other songs till Moeder started beating on the gong in the hall.

"We're starting! . . ." she called.

"Oh, Moekie . . . five more minutes . . ." yelled Ruth, but Jaap and Werner came downstairs, their arms full of big and small parcels, which they piled up at the back door.

Vader came carrying an alarm clock which he put on a plate beside the pile of parcels.

"Do you think they've finished changing?" he whispered.

"The gong was the signal that we're starting," Moeder said in a low voice. "Anyway, we can sit down and start singing."

It took a little while, however, before Ruth and Miep joined them and sat down round the big armchair in the living room. Ruth's cheeks were flushed with the hurrying, and Miep had secret laughing fits, which Gees seemed to catch too.

Moeder started singing, "Zie de maan schijnt door de bomen," and while they were all singing with her, at the top of their voices, a loud ringing suddenly sounded through the house.

Pieter jumped up, with scarlet cheeks, and shouted, "There he is . . . !"

Gees went in to the hall, and Vader threw the door wide open.

"Good evening, Geesje," a voice said, "and how have you been since last year? I see you still have those pretty dimples in your cheeks . . ."

Ruth burst out laughing, but Jaap gave her a violent push.

"Good evening, Sinterklaas," they heard Gees say. "The children are waiting for you. Please come in."

"Welcome, Sinterklaas," said Vader, standing in the doorway, "welcome with all our hearts. I hope it wasn't too cold for you on the heath."

"It's colder than other years," they heard Sinterklaas answer, "but I wanted so much to see the children again, that I just put on an extra undershirt.'

"Do come in," said Vader. "Your chair is all ready." And Sinterklaas entered the room. He was magnificently dressed, all in red and gold. What a beautiful white beard he had, and his crosier was made of genuine gold, you could see that easily. And there was Black Pete too. And he laughed at everybody, threatened with his birch, and held his large bag open for Ruth, who almost fell from her chair laughing. Pieter Pim didn't understand that at all. He wouldn't dare laugh so loud in the presence of Sinterklaas.

"Well, well Meneer and Mevrouw Van Oordt,"

Sinterklaas began, when he was seated in the armchair, "well, well, I hear that your family has increased during the last year. I want to congratulate you on the birth of your little daughter. I would like to see her, but I suppose she is asleep."

"Yes, Sinterklaas," said Vader, while he put his hand on Pieter Pim's head, for Pieter had come creeping to his side. "Yes, Sinterklaas, Anne's asleep already."

"You have another boy, too," Sinterklaas looking at Werner. "My dear boy, I'm glad to see you here. Black Pete told me that he heard you speak Dutch very well."

"Sure, Sinterklaas," said Werner, and Pieter Pim saw that he, too, seemed to be having a lot of fun.

"Good work, my boy. And my faithful valet also told me that you play the violin beautifully. Well, Werner, when I was young, I also played the violin, and I have always thought that one plays better on one's own violin than on somebody else's. Black Pete, come here."

Black Pete held open the big bag for Sinterklaas, who took a large box from it, and gave it to Werner. They all watched breathlessly as Werner unwrapped the paper, and they all shouted "ah . . ." and "oh . . ." when they saw that he had gotten a real violin.

Werner was speechless with surprise. And what was he doing now, Pieter Pim wondered. He thanked Moeder and Vader, instead of Sinterklaas. What a fool, thought Pieter.

Everybody in the family got his turn—a warning, or praise, and a parcel—and it was remarkable how exactly Sinterklaas knew everything. That Ruth dreamed too much at school, that Vader shouldn't forget to talk about the air raid shelters in the Village Council, that Moeder could never find her keys, that Gees shouldn't grumble so much, and that she should bake her delicious pancakes with bacon much more often . . . and so on. And at last it was Pieter's turn. Well, Sinterklaas also knew every secret of his, he even knew about the nail-chewing, so that Pieter almost forgot the words of "*Sinterklaas, kom binnen met je knecht*" which he had to sing for the good Saint. But as a reward he got a pair of those real new, shiny skates with yellow straps. Pieter also kept on looking at Black Pete, who had just the same kind of teeth as Jan, and who, all the time, was whispering things to Ruth and Werner at which they had to laugh terribly. Yes, Pieter Pim's eyes were just bulging. That beautiful golden cross on the Saint's robe, and his pink face that was quite different from other faces (probably because he was so old already) and behind which his eyes rolled in such a funny way. Yes, the Saint had eyes *behind* his face, Pieter thought. Poor Miep had to come and give the Saint a kiss, but she wasn't afraid at all, and gave him a good hug.

"Well," said Sinterklaas at last, "I must be going, else my horse will get impatient, up on the roof. It's awfully cold up there."

They sang another song for Sinterklaas and then Vader accompanied him to the door. Black Pete made a dashing bow before he left, and took off his cap with the beautiful feathers.

"Did you see that, Gees," Pieter Pim whispered later, "Black Pete had blond hair, just like Jan."

"Oh no, my boy," said Gees, "it only looked like that, under the lamplight. It was as black as my oven."

Now the fun really started. They pushed the table back to the center and sat around it. The children took turns bringing a parcel from the pile at the back door. The alarm clock rang every time, and then they shouted, "There, it's ringing again, another parcel . . ." and somebody ran off to get the next present. With each parcel there was a little poem and there were so many "surprises," that Gees got pains in her side with all the laughing she did.

Jan and Maarten had entered inobtrusively. Jan looked definitely queer, with black streaks and red spots all over his face.

"You look just like a zebra," Ruth giggled.

"I couldn't get the black off," Jan whispered.

"What did you use?"

"Pumice stone! Gosh, did it hurt!"

Ruth screamed with laughter. "Imagine, pumice stone!" She tried to tell it to the others, but nobody paid attention to her. Everybody was looking in suspense at Vader, who was trying to get his present out of a bin of coal. It was a dirty job. Vader had rolled up his sleeves, and was looking with despair at the black coals that looked all alike, and between which somebody had hidden his present. Vader also looked suspiciously at Jaap and Werner, who showed a very special interest, and who, with innocent faces, encouraged him to delve deeper. But they got credit for their joke, for the parcel that Vader dug up at last looked so much like a piece of coal that you only knew the difference when you held it in your hand. A clever imitation. Vader, of course, had to go wash his hands and, a moment later, was followed by Moeder, who had fished Jan's present from a jar of starch.

There were enormous parcels which the lucky received in despair. They were wrapped in many layers of paper and tied with lots of string and contained notes that sent the whole family in turns on fruitless errands through the house. There were parcels which went from hand to hand and the contents of which, after all that suspense, landed on the heap of papers and boxes. Even Anne wasn't forgotten, although she wasn't present. And Kees and Zwart both got a new eating trough, from Ruth's Sinterklaas, for which they weren't terribly grateful. They were much more interested in the fat bones Moeder had ordered at the butcher's and which were handed to them very neatly in a parcel. There were poems that exposed all the weak spots of the different persons, little teasing jokes in sugar and chocolate and less edible concoctions. A big bunch of rusty keys for Moeder, who always mislaid her little key-ring.

"Miep's other fiancé," ingeniously composed of Gees' kitchen utensils (the poor soul had been looking for her broom and potato-pan for days), who wore a letter on his chest with a serious warning for Maarten. Calf's brains in a little box for Jan to assist him in his homework, a surprise that was welcomed with cheers by the children, but which was banished from the room by a horrified Moeder. A card file of Dutch words with "Not for use in the drawing room" written on the box, a surprise that Werner received, didn't make a great hit with Moeder either, but she bore it bravely and didn't say anything about it. This evening was the children's evening. An evening of innocent fun, of the joy of receiving and still more the pleasure of giving, an evening of joy because they all belonged together, all of them as they were sitting there, bent over the table under the glow of the lamp. An evening of innocent fun, of solidarity, and of love. A real Dutch evening!

Later the wrappings were cleared away, and they enjoyed the bishops wine, chocolate milk, *speculaas* and *letter-banket*. The children examined each other's presents and ate from the big tins in which each had put away the sweets he had received, chocolate-letters, fondant, *marsepein*, and dolls made of *taai-taai.*

"It was colossal, Moekie," Ruth sighed when Moeder came to tuck her in, "but now we have to wait a whole year again!"

Chapter 9

CHRISTMAS

JUST IMAGINE, the whole family was going to Amsterdam to celebrate Christmas! This is how it came about: *Oma* Van Zuylen and Tante Eef, Moeder's mother and her younger sister, who lived together in a big house at an Amsterdam *gracht*, had invited the boys and Ruth to come and stay with them during the Christmas vacation. But Jaap couldn't leave because of the organ concert he was going to give, Jan had to work, and Ruth . . . yes, actually Ruth could go, but she didn't want to. She had been very much excited when the invitation arrived, but suddenly her big eyes became serious, she closed her little talkative mouth, and in the evening, when Moeder came to say goodnight to her, she said, a little embarrassed, with her head against Moeder's shoulder, "Moekie, I'm not going. I won't leave you on Christmas."

Well, Moeder didn't know what to do. Not that she didn't like to have Jan, Jaap and Ruth around for Christmas, but she wouldn't have enough help during the holidays. She wanted so much to give Gees a vacation to spend Christmas with her old Mother. Gees, who was always at everybody's beck and call, came first this time. But with all the children at home, the baking and the cooking for the festive meals, and looking after Anne, there was too much work for Moeder and Adelheid, the German maid who had come after Sinterklaas.

"What if we should go, all of us, to Amsterdam in the holidays, and take Adelheid with us," Vader proposed.

"I can see myself," said Moeder, "dropping in on Mother with the whole procession."

"Your mother is used to a big family, and there's enough room."

"What about your practice?"

"I'll try to get somebody to take my place. It will do me good to get away for a while."

And so it was decided.

Two days before Christmas the "migration," as Jan called it, took place.

Jaap, Jan and Werner went on the train, the others settled themselves as best they could amidst the luggage in Vader's Chevrolet, and waved a gay farewell to Vader's substitute and Kees and Zwart, who stood looking after them in the doorway.

Pieter Pim was sitting in front between Ruth and Vader, with his nose against the window. Think of it: He was going to Amsterdam! Of course he had told Pieter Pimple and you should have seen his face. "I've been to Belgium, once," he had said. Pieter Pim hadn't the faintest notion whether Belgium was farther away than Amsterdam, but even if he had known, he wouldn't have cared a bit. He was going to Amsterdam and that was the capital of the country. And *Artis* was there, the great zoo. And the puppet-show on the square in front of the Queen's Palace and the *Bijenkorf*, the largest store in the whole country. And the largest soccer stadium in the whole country . . . and he, Pieter Pim, was going to have a look at all that. It was wonderful, but when they were driving through a fir-wood something serious suddenly occurred to him and his face became purple. "Moeder, oh Moeder, we forgot something! . . ." he cried and jumped up in such a hurry that poor Ruth beside him got a terrific smack in the face. "We forgot the Christmas tree . . . and all the candles, and the angels-hair and the big star . . . and everything." Oh, what a shame, thought Pieter, and he expected that Moeder would also be very much upset. But Moeder said quietly. "There'll be a big Christmas tree in Oma's house when you get there this afternoon, Pieter Pim. A big Christmas tree with angel's-hair and candles and a star at the top."

"But do Christmas trees grow in Amsterdam?"

"Not in Amsterdam, but they are brought there in barges. If you want to buy a Christmas tree in Amsterdam, you go to the flower market along the canal and there you'll find them, yours for the choosing. You'll see barges full of Christmas trees."

Pieter felt reassured. Moeder knew the ins and outs of everything, and Pieter turned around to see what Adleheid would say about his clever mother. But Adelheid said nothing at all, only Ruth said something in a very angry voice, for she had gotten another punch, this time in her side. . . .

"Sit still, Pieter Pim, or you'll have to sit in the back,"

Vader warned, and so Pieter Pim sat still for at least five minutes.

Oma's house on the Keizersgracht had a "*stoep*," a real old-fashioned stoep, with stairs, just like all other very old Amsterdam gracht-houses. Stairs on either side of the front door. While Vader parked the car between two trees along the waterside, Jaap, Jan, Werner, Miep and even fat Tante Eef came running down the stoep. Oma appeared, waving, behind the high window near the front door. But Pieter Pim was too sleepy to say hello. His toes lay like dead worms in his shoes, his hands, on which he had been sitting for the last hour, were stiff with cold, and his eyes were little sleepy slits. Driving in a car was all right, but it shouldn't last a whole afternoon. Anne didn't like it much either, and was crying at the top of her little lungs.

Yes, Oma's house was old, as old as the time when rich and stately merchants sat behind that typical high and narrow window beside the front door, and looked out over the *grachten*, where the barges came and went, loaded with goods from distant countries. That was in the seventeenth century, the Golden Century, the century of the East Indies Company. Maybe one of the gentlemen who had managed the East Indies Company had sat behind that very window from which Oma was now waving. One of the seventeen gentlemen who sent the ships to the East Indies and watched through that window for the messenger who came and told him that his ships, great and proud sailing ships, had put into port, and were now waiting on the river IJ to be unloaded. Ships full of spices, sugar, and other exotic treasures. And a few days later that same *Heer* would have been sitting behind his window, watching the barges being unloaded, the merchandise being hoisted on the "Gallows," the crane over the dormer-window that opened outwards. Oh yes, Oma's house was that old. It had a wide marble hall, leading to the *zaal achter*, the large panelled room at the back of the house where the merchant's family used to gather for meals and prayers. The *zaal achter*, with the purple leaded windows, through which you looked out on the yard with the marble statues. There was also a basement with a large bright kitchen, where the shining copper pots and pans hung around the chimney. The house had heavily beamed ceilings, and narrow stairs with a sculptured bannister leading to the floors above.

Of course the house was too big for Oma and Tante Eef alone, but it had been just large enough when Opa and Oma were young and there were ten children.

And now? . . . Now it was just big enough too, for, as Oma used to say, "My family keeps on growing." After Opa's death, when Moeder and her sisters and brothers had left the house, all except Tante Eef, Oma had started to take young girls into her home. Mostly children from the Indies, who went to school in Holland. "And I kept up with the times," Oma always said, very proudly, because later she had also taken boys into the house. Boys and girls who came to study or work in Amsterdam. They were a gay lot, there in Oma's house, although the doctor had forbidden her during the past few years to take in more than five "foster-children."

Only in the summer and during Christmas vacations was the house quiet. Then they were "childless," as Tante Eef put it.

"Aren't we too many for you, Mother?" Moeder asked after the greetings were over.

"I'll tell you something," Oma said confidentially, "I hate those long vacations . . . it's much too quiet for me here. I'm really glad that you came. Otherwise I would surely have come to you."

When Pieter Pim had drunk a glass of milk, he was revived to such a degree that he could inspect the Christmas tree, and later at dinner he did most of the talking. Even when his mouth was full of string beans and sausage . . .

He told Oma in great detail about Hein Uienkruier, Gezina, and Pieter Pimple. Tante Eef shook with laughter, so Pieter Pim, encouraged by his success, told more and more stories, things that really never had happened, but that made Tante Eef sigh with pleasure all the same. But before Pieter could get too excited, he was put to bed in one of the high-ceilinged old bedrooms. Anne was already quietly asleep in Oma's laundry basket, decorated in her honor with mistletoe and red ribbons.

Downstairs the older ones grouped themselves around the roaring stove in Oma's sitting-room.

There was so much to tell and Oma was interested in everything. Above all she wanted to hear all about the organ concert that Jaap had given. A beautiful concert because of which Jaap had become known in the whole village as an organist. They had raised more than three hundred guilders and Jaap himself was going to hand the money over to the committee, which had its head office in Amsterdam.

They stayed up very late that night, and Ruth fell asleep on the foot-stool near the stove.

The next morning at breakfast the plans for the day were discussed.

Pieter Pim had more wishes than anybody else. "I want to see the Christmas trees at the canal, and the puppet-show on the Dam, and the Queen's Palace, and Artis, and the IJ, and I want to go to the museum with the old flags, and to Zandvoort, to the beach . . ." He was really indignant when the whole family burst into laughter.

"And Ruth?" Oma asked.

"The *Kalverstraat*, Oma, where all the beautiful shops are, and the Bijenkorf, and I would simply love to help trim the Christmas tree."

"And Werner?"

"I'd like to go to the Committee for Jewish Refugees," Werner said.

"Werner must also go to the American consul about his papers," Vader said. "We must see to it that he goes to America as soon as possible. His uncle there is waiting for him."

"Yes," Werner said. He had been eating his thick oatmeal porridge with relish but now he moved his spoon very slowly from his plate to his mouth, so slowly that the porridge became starchy and unappetizing.

Jan wanted to go the Museum of Navigation and to the famous Amsterdam harbor.

Moeder proposed to go with Pieter Pim and Ruth. Vader and Oma said that they would like to go with them. Tante Eef and Jan would go to the museum, and Jaap and Werner set off together. Miep phoned that she had to work but that she would come in the afternoon to help trim the Christmas tree.

Pieter Pim was in such a hurry to get away that he almost choked on his porridge. After breakfast, however, his patience was put to a severe test. Oma and Tante Eef and Moeder had a lot of things to do before they could leave, and so Pieter Pim looked out of the window at the people hurrying along the *grachten* to their work. It had snowed the night before, and in the center of town it had become very slushy. The cars splashed mud on the pedestrians. A man on a bicycle skidded at the corner and was thrown quite a distance against the legs of a passing lady. Pieter thought that hilarious. The man who had scrambled up in the meantime and who happened to look up at the window at which Pieter was standing, couldn't understand why Pieter stuck out his tongue at him. Well, to be exact, Pieter didn't understand that either!

At last, everybody was ready to go and a moment later they were on their way. Heavens, how crowded it was! In the *Leidsestraat* the yellow trolley cars rode to and fro and the people hurried along on their bicycles. The cars were hooting loud enough to burst your eardrums, and heavily loaded barges were tooting while passing underneath the bridges on their way to the warehouses, where they would be unloaded.

Pieter Pim got a stiff neck with all the sightseeing he did. He completely forgot to watch out for the traffic, so that he kept stepping off the sidewalk and almost got knocked down by the cyclists who rushed close to the curb. They couldn't get Ruth away from the shop windows, and the passersby smiled at her excited exclamations.

They walked through the Kalverstraat, the street in Amsterdam where most of the stores are, and then they came to the Dam. There stood the Queen's Palace, the large grey building with many, many windows. Now it was closed, not even a sentry was on guard. The Queen lived in The Hague, and only when she paid her yearly visit to Amsterdam were the shutters opened and sentries posted. Then the whole square would be full of people who hoped to see the Queen on the balcony. They would serenade her and the famous chime player, Vincent, played national songs. While they were walking over the square, Vader told them about those visits of the Queen and he showed them "the Little Stones" in front of the Palace, where nobody was allowed to walk when the Queen was in town, except the sentries. He also told them that the Palace was built on piles, like all other houses in Amsterdam, because the ground was so soggy. Under the Palace there were as many piles as there were days in the year, with a 1 before and a 9 behind it! "13,659 piles," Ruth figured quickly.

"Do you know," said Vader, "that here under the ground of Amsterdam there is a whole forest, a forest of piles. Millions of piles that have been driven into the ground one by one; they used to do it by hand, later with a pulley-block, and nowadays with an engine driven pulley-block. If they didn't drive those piles into the ground, the houses would sink into the marshy ground, you see."

The puppet-show wasn't there. "I suppose it's too cold," Moeder said. Usually it stood there, on the square, and all day long children would gather in front of the little puppet theater and laugh and shout at the adventures of Jan Klaassen and Pieternel, and the children who had a few pennies didn't at all mind giving them to the woman who passed the cup.

Pieter was very disappointed, but, luckily, across the square was the Bijenkorf, where you could buy anything. "Even puppet-shows," Vader said to comfort him. He took Pieter straight to the toy department while Moeder, Oma and Ruth went shopping. Later they had a cup of hot chocolate in the restaurant. Pieter Pim and Ruth had never seen a store as big as this. It made them feel all funny and drowsy. But after Pieter had licked his cup clean he was ready to go to Artis.

They went to Artis and Pieter Pim couldn't look long enough at the monkeys and lions. But Ruth grew very quiet and said that she thought it was so horrid, all those animals in cages. Other children made the big brown bear dance, but Ruth almost cried, she was so sorry for the poor beast. "Just imagine, Moeder," she said, "just imagine that you are a big, strong animal like that and have to dance because small girls and boys, I mean girls and boys who are so much smaller than that bear, want to laugh."

No, Ruth didn't like it at all in Artis, and she was glad to go home with Oma to help trim the Christmas tree. Pieter Pim was going to have lunch in town with Vader and Moeder, in a real restaurant and he could choose what he wanted to eat. That had never happened to him before.

Vader took them to *De Poort van Cleef*, a big restaurant at the back of the Queen's Palace.

Moeder was as much excited as Pieter. She clasped Vader's arm and pinched Pieter's hand and said, "I haven't been there for fifteen years!" Pieter was in such a hurry to get in, that he almost got stuck in the revolving door, but once he was inside and seated at a neatly laid little table, his nose just visible above the edge, he felt smaller than a little bird in a grown-up hand and he didn't even say peep. And if he had said peep, nobody would have been able to hear him. The noise was ear-splitting.

Vader had to laugh at his scared face. "What a noise, eh, Pieter? This is a very famous restaurant; it's older than the three of us together and it's famous the whole world over. Listen to the waiters. Do you hear what they are shouting?" Pieter pricked up his ears and when he found out where all that noise came from, sat right up in his chair so he would look more like a person who's afraid of nobody. The waiters repeated the orders they received at the top of their voices, and behind the buffet stood a man who shouted each order again through a wicket beside him. "Two pork chops with spinaaaaaaach . . . and potatoes . . ." the waiter shouted, and the man at the wicket repeated it with a beautiful drawn-out cry after 'chop' and 'spinach.' "That shouting is a peculiarity of De Poort van Cleef," Vader told him. "Here only waiters with good, clear voices can serve. Don't you think that's interesting, Pieter?"

Yes, indeed, Pieter thought it was interesting, and when the waiter came to their table to take the order, Pieter Pim shouted as loud and as beautifully as he could, through the whole restaurant, "Steak . . . fried potatoes . . . and peas . . ." and the waiter repeated it even more beautifully, and louder, while the man at the wicket also did his utmost. Pieter was as proud as a peacock. He had fixed that nicely. The people in the restaurant had great fun, and so did Vader, but Moeder turned scarlet and quickly tied a large white napkin round Pieter's neck with the knot neatly behind his ears.

"When I'm grown-up I'm going to live in Amsterdam," Pieter said later, when he had swallowed the last mouthful of chocolate pudding with whipped cream. "You can have adventures here." And he looked so enterprising that on the way home, Moeder didn't let go of his hand one single moment.

In the big grachten-house the preparations for Christmas evening were in full swing. Already, in the front hall you could smell the sweet, warm odor of pastry, and the spicy fragrance of fir. The stately zaal achter with its lovely antique furniture was just the right place in which to celebrate Christmas. It had always been the place. How often had small, industrious hands put holly and mistletoe around the pictures and over the doorways, pushed thick fat candles in the ancient copper brackets and fixed small red candles in shiny red apples! Small hands had arranged fruits and nuts on the pewter dishes and rubbed the refectory table in the nook near the chimney with a woollen cloth, so it would reflect the candles. This time Ruth had done these chores and her cheeks were rosy with excitement and fatigue.

Miep, Jan and Tante Eef trimmed the Christmas tree. It was such a tall one that Ruth couldn't have reached it anyway; even Miep had to stand on a step-ladder to fasten the silver star to the top.

"You see, Moeder," Ruth called eagerly, "only silver and white on the Christmas tree! That's the prettiest. Don't you think it looks really . . . really holy?" she asked with a shy little smile.

Pieter Pim and Ruth were sent to bed for a nap because they were going to stay up late and Moeder disappeared straight away to the basement to help with the baking and the cooking.

Before Ruth went for her nap she pulled Vader's coat. "Vader, when you read from the Bible tonight and Oma says, 'Amen,' will you read on a little farther to where Mary says that, you know. . . ."

"Of course I will darling."

"I think that's the most beautiful of all, Vader, I don't know why."

That night they were all sitting in a corner of the large zaal achter under soft candlelight. At the far end of the room the Christmas tree threw a circle of light on the beams. And Vader read the words they all knew because he read them every year. Ruth was sitting close to Moeder, and again she thought that this was the best hour of the whole year, this hour, and that she wouldn't miss it for anything in the world, and she listened. . . .

. . . And the Angel said unto them, Fear not: for, behold, I bring you good tidings of great joy, which shall be to all people. For unto you is born this day in the city of David a Saviour, which is Christ the Lord. And this shall be a sign unto you; ye shall find the babe wrapped in swaddling clothes, lying in a manger. . . .
. . . Glory to God in the highest, and on earth peace, good will toward men. . . .

"Amen," Oma said softly. Vader looked up, and as he saw Ruth's devout little face, he read on, to

. . . But Mary kept all these things, and pondered them in her heart. . . . Amen. . . .

"That's that . . ." said Pieter, sighing with relief. "Now we're going to eat the candy from the tree."

"Oh no, we're going to sing first." Tante Eef got the song book and Jaap sat down at the piano, without anybody having to ask him to. And then all of them, in a circle around him, joined in singing the old Dutch Christmas carols. Oma, in her tremulous voice started the songs, the others followed, and Ruth's voice, very high and clear, rose above all the others. Maarten, Vader and Moeder sang the second voice. Pieter Pim hummed, in his own way. Quite different from what was in the book, but quite audibly, you may be sure.

"Please tell Pieter to be quiet," Ruth complained. "He spoils it all."

"Be tolerant, Ruth," Moeder warned. But luckily Pieter Pim got tired of the singing and went to the tree to see to it that it wouldn't catch fire. At the same time he ate the little chocolate garlands that had dropped. When you touched the tree they fell to the floor all by themselves, and Pieter didn't like to have any mess lying around on the floor on holidays. No, indeed!

Later the others came to join him and sat down, while Jaap played for them. They drank tea and ate *Kerstkrans*, Christmas cake. They talked in low voices, and when Pieter had gone to bed, Vader read to them from the Christmas stories of Selma Lagerlöf.

"If only it could always be Christmas," Ruth told Moeder as she was getting into bed, "then people would always be good to each other and there would never be another war."

The first Christmas day flew by. In the morning the whole family, big and small, went to the church on the Dam.

This was quite different from attending church in the village, in familiar surroundings. There they knew everybody—Look, there's Aldewaal, he's well again. . . . And there's Dirk too, he must be on leave from the army. . . . Marietje has a new hat. . . . The notary isn't here, probably still has a cold.—Yes, that's the way it was in the village. But here there were nothing but strange faces. And what a crowd! They had trouble finding seats, and couldn't even sit together. During the Christmas season Amsterdam was full of tourists, many of whom liked to attend the service in the old church on the Dam. The Christmas service in the morning was as famous as the early mass, or rather the midnight mass, in the Moses-and-Aaron Church, where even those who were not Catholics would come on Christmas Eve "to rock the Infant."

After the service the children pushed and jostled to get out, for Oma had promised that she would show them old-Amsterdam and they couldn't wait to see it. For who could show them better than Oma, who had lived here all her life!

Today the small, narrow grachten, the little high bridges, and the city ramparts were recovering from the everyday noise. On week-days there was a hustle and bustle that made your head whirl and such noise that you couldn't hear your own words. Trucks that rattled over the bumpy cobble-stones, pushcarts which couldn't make the steep little bridges, and yet landed on the other side with the aid of bystanders. Cars that hooted a warning at sharp corners and narrow curves.

Street-sellers who advertised their wares. The tooting of the boats . . . the creaking of the cranes that hoisted the goods into the warehouses. The ringing of the bells on the many, many bicycles. It wasn't for nothing, said Oma, that an Anti-Noise Association had been set up in Amsterdam.

But now, on Sunday, old-Amsterdam looked just like a stage backdrop. In a moment the curtain would rise and the play would start. Old, shaky little houses leaned tiredly against each other and dreamed of centuries long past. Perhaps a door would open and ladies and gentlemen in colorful sixteenth century costumes would appear. . . . Oma could tell it all so wonderfully, and the children, afraid to miss a single word, pushed so close around her that they tripped over each other's feet. "When those little houses are in danger of collapsing, the people are not allowed to live there any longer, and a sign is nailed on the door saying, 'This dwelling is declared unfit for tenants . . .' " Oma said, as she showed them a shaky little house with nailed-up shutters that was leaning against a newer house like a sick child against its mother.

Oma took them to the *Westermarkt*, where the oldest and highest church stood, the *Lange Jan*, as the people call it, whose square tower rose high above the old irregular roofs of the *Jordaan*. The tower had been built in 1620 by the famous architect Hendrick de Keyser. On the top of the tower stood the golden king's-crown, on top of that the golden ball, and on top of that the golden cross, and on top of the cross stood the little weather-cock. On this first of the two Christmas days the weather was nice and clear and all the gold was sparkling in the sun.

They saw the *Montelbaanstoren*, built in 1613 by the same architect, which used to be a part of the city ramparts, as did the *Munttoren*. There were so many towers in Amsterdam that it was impossible to see them all in one morning. Each had a carillon, and throughout the year, at certain hours, the air was filled with the music of chimes.

They walked along the city ramparts, little grachten, almost too narrow for a car, imprisoned between old, very old little houses with decorated façades. There were the small wooden bridges with iron rails, paved with uneven, bumpy cobble-stones. They saw the backs of the houses on the *Zeedijk*, where the water washed over the little jetties. How old and dilapidated and unkempt it all was, and yet people lived there, just as they lived four centuries ago! Here and there stood a new house among the old ones, but it didn't belong there and the old houses seemed to turn a little away from it.

"You shouldn't come here at night; it's dangerous then," Oma told them. "They call it 'Dark Amsterdam.' All kinds of things happen—thefts, robberies, fights; all the rough customers from the ships and the docks come here. And, just think, not so far away in South Amsterdam, are the very modern apartment houses, decorated with figures by famous Dutch sculptors, yes, as modern as you'll find anywhere in Northern Europe. Houses for both the poor and the rich, modern and comfortable. It's indeed a big improvement over this part of the town."

"That's just like you and me, Oma," said Pieter Pim seriously. "You're old, with wrinkles, and I'm smooth, 'cause I'm young, you see."

"Oh, Pieter . . ." cried Ruth, startled. "He doesn't know what he's saying, Omatje. Don't listen to him!"

But Oma laughed. "He's quite right, Ruthie; it's just as he says."

After they had been at the docks with the large ships, and the huge cranes, Ruth asked if they could now see the *Begijnenhofje*. So Vader treated them to a taxi because they were all so tired.

The *Begijnenhofje* was a small, quiet island in the midst of one of the busiest parts of town. Here lived the old women who, being poor and without relatives, had found a home in this ancient court. It was so quiet that, as Ruth said, "You had to walk on tiptoe."

In front of the houses were small gardens, and behind the clean little curtains the women were drinking their morning coffee.

"I'd like a cup of coffee, too," said Oma. "Who's coming . . . we're very near home now."

"And Rembrandt's house?" Jaap asked.

"Some other time," Oma promised, "I'm exhausted."

In the afternoon they stayed at home. Then the uncles and aunts, and the cousins, and nephews and nieces came to visit. They played games and they lighted the tree again. After that marvelous afternoon Pieter told everybody who wanted to listen that he wouldn't go home any more, and would stay with Oma and Tante Eef. And that was that. At home he didn't have anybody but Pieter Pimple to play with, a good-for-nothing, while here he had heaps of cousins. Cousins in knee-socks, cousins who were Boy Scouts, even though they weren't three months older than he. And a girl cousin, Liesje, with blond braids, who could find the best spots when playing hide-and-seek, and who was afraid of nobody, not even of Stien and Bep in Oma's kitchen.

No, Pieter Pim was determined to stay in Amsterdam, and the only reason why he went home, after all, was because Moeder had invited Liesje to go with them.

Chapter 10

RUTH AGAIN

RUTH'S CLASS was very restless. Perhaps because it was the first day that felt like spring. The weather wasn't fine, oh, no, but the snow had melted, and the children could bicycle to school again. To be able to do that . . . to race and feel the wind in your face, the air of spring all around you! Through the school window they saw the sky become bluer, the clouds thinner and smaller. Perhaps the sun would come out in a moment and dry up the puddles. Ruth thought today was worse than ever. She felt so tired and funny. Maybe it was spring-fever, as people called it.

Heavens, how boring that arithmetic lesson was!

The lesson went on and on. The last ten minutes seemed longer to Ruth than the whole hour. If only they would let her do the problems, for she had long understood what the teacher was explaining.

When Ruth was bored in school she would let her thoughts wander all over the place. If only . . . she started to dream very pleasantly and her eyes rested on the geraniums on the window sills, the collar on juffrouw Ditmar's dress, Christien's red curls. But she didn't want to look at the school-maps. Those were *too* ugly. Then her thoughts returned to school, how long every day lasted, and how tedious it was. . . .

She had to take care that she didn't stare, she had to keep her eyes awake, then it wouldn't be noticed.

There were children who liked school. Elly, for instance, because she was best. There were children who hated it, because they couldn't keep up with the others and always got bad reports. Ruth could keep up quite well; actually she could have been the best in the class, but she didn't want to. It was nicer to dream. And anyway, Elly was the best, wasn't she? Ruth didn't care to be the best one. She wanted other things, of which she dreamed, but never spoke. She wanted to be a writer. But they would laugh at her if she told them. When she handed in a composition, her heart would beat fast. And once she had handed one in, she felt embarrassed, as if she had told somebody something that was too personal. Mostly she found an "excellent" under her compositions, or "did you think of that yourself?" She *had* thought of it herself. Certainly she had. At home she also wrote stories, but these she slipped in an old writing case Moeder had given her, a writing case with a lock on it.

Elly couldn't write compositions, and Ruth tried very hard not to be pleased about it. . . .

If only this period was over. Then they would have Language, and they would get back their compositions which had been corrected.

"Ruth, are you asleep? I asked you something, Ruth."

See, now she would catch it. Now her eyes hadn't stayed awake; she had begun staring into the teacher's face. "What did I say last, Ruth?"

From several directions the children tried to whisper it to her, but Ruth had already given up. "I don't know," she said.

"Who can repeat for Ruth what I said?"

Of course Elly held up her finger, and Ruth had to face her, as she repeated the teacher's last words.

"Teacher said . . ." Elly started emphatically. Ruth didn't listen to what else she said. She just looked at Elly's laughing triumphant face. It looked almost ugly with that smug expression on it. Ruth turned her head away. She suddenly felt sick. Oh, if she only could go home!

Juffrouw Van Steenbergen herself gave the language lesson this time because one of the teachers was ill.

She started handing the compositions back. Ruth gasped, when she had her work in front of her. It was full of red ink lines and corrections. Language: 3; style: 9; was written under it. Ten was the highest mark.

"A lot of mistakes, Ruth," said juffrouw Van Steenbergen.

"I didn't pay attention to the spelling at all," Ruth admitted.

"You were very much absorbed in your story, while you were writing it, weren't you?"

"Yes," Ruth nodded, with scarlet cheeks.

"You can come and read it for the class. It's a very nice composition."

"Oh, no," Ruth started, "no, I can't do that. Oh, no, please."

The children laughed at Ruth, who looked so frightened, all huddled up on her bench.

Juffrouw Van Steenbergen smiled. "Well, then I will read it."

And so she read the composition for them, while Ruth, with all her courage, held her head high and kept looking right in front of her.

After school Elly called the girls of the class together. "I'm going to give a party," she said. "Saturday afternoon, at half past two."

"You didn't tell me anything about it," said Christien, who was Elly's friend. "Why didn't you tell me?"

"Didn't I tell you?" Elly said, casually. "Must have forgotten."

While Ruth was slowly walking home, she puzzled over Elly. She had immediately understood that Elly hadn't intended to invite the girls. She had only thought of it after Ruth's composition had been read. Ruth knew that. She knew that she had been the cause, but why, she didn't quite understand.

Ruth thought about it until she got home, but then she forgot her worries. Pieter Pim was standing at the dormer-window, all red with excitement, and shouting and waving. "Come, quick, quick, so wonderful . . . oh, please come . . ." and a whole lot more that Ruth couldn't understand.

"What?"

Pieter yelled his message all over again, but Ruth didn't feel like going all the way upstairs. Her legs felt so tired.

"You'd better do as he asks," laughed Jaap, who pushed the gate open with his bicycle. Ruth looked at him. It seemed as if his face and everything around was dotted with black spots.

Zwart had had kittens, three grey little balls, as small as mice. Pieter Pim had found them in the attic closet, on the Dutch flag, of all things! Ruth tried to touch them, but Zwart laid a protecting paw over her offspring and looked at Ruth in an unfriendly manner. "I've thought of three names for them already," Pieter said proudly. "Rood, Wit and Blauw, just like the flag." Ruth burst out laughing, but Jaap, who came to have a look too, said they were very nice names.

"That cat family is sure to represent all the colors of the rainbow, if things continue. *Rood, wit* and *blauw* indeed!" said Moeder, who came with a little plate of liver. "Here, Zwart, eat this; it'll give you back your strength," she said. But Zwart didn't move.—You'd better go first, all of you—she was surely thinking—I don't dare to leave my children alone now.—Kees also came upstairs, and started sniffing at the kittens. Apparently Zwart didn't mind that at all.

"She trusts Kees more than us," Ruth said with indignation.

"Maybe she's right," said Moeder, "at least I know who wants to take those little kittens in her hands all the time, which is very bad for them."

"Oh no, not me."

"Whom the cap fits, let wear it," Jaap teased.

"Come, Jaap, help me pull that flag from under the cats," Moeder asked. "Pieter, give me that old flower basket, and we'll fix up the Zwart family a little better. And Ruth, you'd better take the flag to the village to the cleaners. You can take Pieter Pim along, but come back right away, mind you. We'll have dinner at six sharp."

Ruth and Pieter Pim went along the heath path with Kees trotting behind them. The days were lengthening and you could smell the spring in the air. There was the smell of the earth being ploughed up, the budding trees, and the soil drying, at last, under the warmer sun.

It was very quiet on the heath. Only the children's steps and Kees' barking could be heard.

Pieter grasped Ruth's hand. "When I'm grown-up," he said confidentially, "I'm going to marry a lady just like Moeder, but then I'll have three children all at once, just like Zwart. 'Cause if those children are born at the same time, they can play together."

Ruth didn't know what to answer. If somebody else had been with her, they could have laughed about Pieter together, but when you were alone with him you couldn't.

"In a few years you'll be able to play with Anne," she said.

"If she'll be like Liesje," Pieter said.

"Yes, but Liesje is very wild," Ruth said. "Remember how she flooded the cellar?"

When you went to the village with Pieter Pim, you had to keep his stopping-places in mind. Pieter had fixed stations of interest. First, on the sand path a little candy shop, the paradise of juffrouw Mes. He always wanted to go in to buy a piece of tape-licorice or a color-ball. The funny part of it was that Pieter only bought the sweets when he was with somebody else, never from his own pocket money. The others all had more pocket money than he had, and he was saving his for a "Flying Dutchman," you know, a small cart that you drove with a lever. Pieter Pim had already saved thirty cents. . . .

Ruth knew quite well that she couldn't avoid it, so, although she didn't feel like it at all today, she walked right into juffrouw Mes' shop with Pieter Pim. Juffrouw Mes' size was in no relation whatsoever to the size of her little store. Besides, it wasn't exactly clean inside, and very untidy. But what did it matter; she had a delicious collection of candies. Bright-colored lollypops and drops. Toffees in shiny paper, pineapple balls, raspberry-drops, and, best of all, color-balls. A little ball that changed colors several times, and that, therefore, you took out of your mouth, time and again, so you could see the miracle. You got a lot for your one cent. Once your capital had landed safe and sound in the woman's cash-drawer, she stuck her grubby hand, with the particularly long and black nail on her little finger, into the bottle of your choice. One by one the little candies were counted out in your hand, and whatever remained, juffrouw Mes put in her own mouth.

As the second stopping place of fun Pieter always wanted to cross the unguarded railroad crossing. When he went alone to the village it was forbidden ground, and he had to make a detour; he then used the crossing that was guarded. That was no fun at all, for, if a train was coming, the signalman lowered the barriers, but at the other crossing you had to push open the gate yourself, and the trains rushed right past you.

After that was finished Pieter had to pass the lumber mill, and finally he wanted to go and look at the pictures in front of the village movie house. At the end of all that Ruth really felt funny. She wanted to cry, and to shout at Pieter.

But at last they did get to juffrouw Schevedeur's store. Kees wasn't allowed to go in there, for juffrouw Schevedeur was afraid of dogs.

"Well, Ruth," she asked "are you going to knit another sweater?"

"No," Ruth said. And while the woman wrote out the receipt for the flag, Ruth looked at the things that were lying on the counters. On one side of the little store juffrouw Schevedeur sold cigars and such and at the other counter notions. That's why the notions smelt of tobacco, and the tobacco had the somewhat stale smell of notions.

In one of the compartments along the wall juffrouw Schevedeur had arranged rolls of ribbon. It was a terrific tangle of colors, for in addition to the cigars and cigarettes and the yarn and buttons, the woman had four children and a husband who was unemployed, so she had little time to tidy up the shop. But Ruth saw that the ribbons were beautiful. Ribbons with checks and with flowers. Juffrouw Schevedeur, who followed the direction of her glance, told her that it was the "newest thing." Just arrived from town.

"Lovely for your hair, Ruth, if you go to a party. Your curls are just long enough for two grips with bows," she said.

"Yes," Ruth said, a little shy.

"I heard that there is going to be a party at Elly Verschuren's. You know Elly, don't you? She is going to have a new dress for it. She just came in with her mother to buy the material."

"I'm going, too," Ruth said.

"Then you should ask your mother for a couple of bows," the woman said. "That looks very smart, Ruth. What color dress will you wear?"

"Green," said Ruth, "with a flowered jacket."

The woman took a ribbon from the compartment and spread it out for Ruth. "Here, look, exactly what you need, Ruth. A little pink flower on a green background."

Ruth nodded. She didn't know what to say, but she could see herself already with the bows on either side of her face. It would be lovely.

"It is only a *kwartje* a yard," juffrouw Schevedeur said.

"Is a yard enough?" asked Ruth breathlessly.

"Oh, more than enough. Three-quarters is sufficient."

"Then . . . then . . . I'll have it," Ruth said excitedly.

"I'll bring the money tomorrow. I've got it in my piggy bank."

"Come on now," Pieter Pim said. "We'll be late for supper." He had seen everything in the shop by now and he wanted to go home.

"You run along," said Ruth who didn't want anything to interfere with this buying treat. And as Pieter Pim slipped out of the store Ruth watched the woman unwind the ribbon, measure it out and cut it.

Holding the parcel tightly in her hand, she left the store, and outside, under a street lamp she had another good look at her newly acquired treasure.

But then the village bell struck. Six beats. Suppertime! She would be much too late and Pieter was nowhere to be seen. He had started running, of course. And he wasn't allowed on the road alone at night. If only Kees had stayed with him! Ruth began to run. The village street was quiet, people were having dinner now. You could see them sitting in their houses, under their lamps. They all had the same lamp, with an orange or red shade hanging low over the table. Ruth trotted along the road to catch up with Pieter, but though she was otuside the village now, she still didn't see him.

If only he hadn't crossed the unguarded railroad crossing! She stopped for a moment, her heart was beating fast, her palms tingling, her sides hurt terribly. At ten minutes past six the local would pass, the same local in which Jaap came home from town, when he had his piano lesson. And the gates of the crossing were difficult to open. Oh, if only Pieter had gone in the other direction! Maybe he wouldn't cross. He didn't in the day time, so why should he do it now? She slowed down, she was worrying about nothing. She tried to think about the ribbons. They really were very smart, just as juffrouw Schevedeur had said. It would make the girls sit up. They would play games of forfeits, and hide and seek, Elly would play her gramophone, and they would dance. Already Ruth saw herself walking through Verschuren's big house with the bows on either side of her face.—Oh, Ruth, how wonderful—the girls would say—how lovely you look.—And Elly . . . she would look at her just as she had done this afternoon at school when her composition had been read aloud. . . . Suddenly Ruth knew that Elly was jealous of her. Yes, that's what it was. That's why she had invited the girls. And that's what why she, Ruth, had bought the ribbons. To make Elly jealous. It suddenly made Ruth very sad. . . .

Then she heard the whistle of the train, and started to run again. She ran as if she were racing with the train to see who would reach the crossing first. It was getting dark now. Ruth ran. . . .

She heard barking, and out of the dusk, Kees jumped up at her. But Ruth pushed him away. "Where is Pieter, where is he?" she panted. If Kees is here, she thought, then Pieter must also have gone this way. It's my fault, the fault of the ribbons. "Pieter . . ." she called, "Pieter . . ."

Through the trees the fire-eyes of the train approached. . . . When she was close to the crossing she saw Pieter sitting on the gate. Ruth stopped with a thumping heart. She didn't dare call him, he might start, and fall. The train passed him. It was the local, but how big it seemed now, when you stood so close to it. And what a noise it made! When the last car had passed, she ran up to Pieter. He was sitting there, very satisfied with himself. But Ruth burst into tears. "You nasty boy," she cried, "you know you shouldn't cross here."

"Can you imagine that," he shouted in great indignation, "I haven't crossed it, have I, stupid!" Ruth pulled him roughly from the gate, grasped his collar, and started running home. Pieter, feeling very much wronged, and also in tears, ran with her, stumbling over his own feet.

They made such a pitiful entry into the living room, that Moeder didn't scold them about their being late. Ruth was terribly upset, and she couldn't even tell Moeder why.

Chapter 11

RUTH IS ILL

PIETER PIM was sitting on the stairs with his elbows on his knees. He was in everybody's way there. Moeder had already told him a few times that he'd better go to the living room. But Pieter stayed where he was. Sitting there, he didn't feel so lonely.

It was gloomy in the house. Upstairs Ruth was lying

in her little room. Vader hadn't gone out yesterday nor today. He sat at Ruth's bedside all the time. Moeder and Adelheid were continuously running up and down the stairs. They carried all kinds of things to and fro. There had also been a strange doctor in the house, and Vader had talked with him for a long time, while they were walking up and down the garden path.

When he passed him, later, on his way up, he put his hand for a moment on Pieter's blond head and Pieter asked, "Shall I go and beat up an egg for Ruth, Vader?" because he could do that so well, and they always let him do it when somebody in the house was sick.

But no, no eggs to beat. Vader had smiled for a moment. Pieter didn't know why, for he wasn't happy. You could easily see that. It wasn't unusual for grown-up people to laugh, even if they weren't gay. Grown-up people also said "I'm so glad you came" to elegant visitors, when they were lying on the couch, nice and lazy, with slippers on and a little jacket with holes in it, and a magazine from the weekly reading case. Grown-up people did act strangely sometimes, and Pieter knew that he had to learn a whole lot of things before he would be grown-up himself.

At other times Pieter liked to be in the kitchen, but now . . . gosh now, Gees walked about sniffing. Her face was all spotty from crying, and she had put the flower basket with Zwart, Rood, Wit and Blauw, in the garden. Fancy, in the rain, in the nasty drizzle.

No, this was not the right day to go to Gees.

Pieter sighed. The grandfather-clock was ticking words. Tic-tac, yes-no, poor Ruth. The hands moved very slowly. Pieter turned his back to them. If only he dared to take Zwart and her little ones inside. They were getting all wet. A big tear trickled down Pieter's left cheek. He caught it with his tongue.

Tic-tac, yes-no, poor Ruth. . . .

Then he heard the gate creak and a moment later Gees' voice. "No cats in my kitchen today!" And Werner, who answered, "All right, Gees, I'll take them to my room." Gees grumbled something else, but Werner didn't seem to pay attention, for he came into the hall with the cats' basket.

"Hello, Werner," Pieter said, and licked a tear from his right cheek.

Werner gave him a searching look. "Coming to my room?" he asked then. "You can help me."

Pieter rubbed his nose clean with his hand, and tip-toed behind Werner. When they passed Ruth's room, they heard her talk.

"Ruth is talking again," Pieter whispered hopefully. "Is she better?"

"Not yet," Werner said. "She is talking in her sleep, you see."

"Oh." Pieter sat down on the edge of Werner's bed.

Werner sat down beside him with an exercise book. "You can help me with my homework," he said.

That cheered Pieter up. Oh, boy, homework, what more do you want? . . . This proved that there were people who knew that Pieter Pim wasn't such a small boy after all.

Werner opened his copy book and pointed with his pencil to something at the top of the page. "I wrote there," said Werner, " 'Many people in Holland live on boots'—and the teacher put a line under it."

"It should be boats," Pieter said proudly. "Boots is wrong."

"And here I wrote . . ." Werner continued, " 'The ships go on the canals.' "

"It's sail," Pieter corrected.

" 'The people and children sleep and eat in the cabin. The children are born and grow on the water.' "

"Children don't grow on the water, stupid," said Pieter, who began to find himself more clever every moment.

"Then what should it be?" Werner asked.

"Just think hard," said Pieter, who now imagined himself to be the teacher, and Werner the student.

Werner got his dictionary and looked it up. "It's 'to grow up,' " he said.

"Good," Pieter nodded, satisfied.

"Then what should it be in this sentence?"

"If you use your brains, you can find it easily," said Pieter who didn't know it himself.

"Let's go on, anyway," Werner proposed. " 'Those

boats, or *tjalken*, bring goods through the whole country. They used to be pulled by dogs or horses, even by men, but nowadays most of them have engines,' " Werner read. " 'Bring' is wrong."

Pieter, who now acted the part of teacher completely, nodded his head seriously. "You did that very badly, Werner," he said.

"Yes, teacher," Werner said, ashamed.

—See—Pieter Pim thought—you could really play with Werner. A good thing that he hadn't gone to America, and would stay with them until the war was over.—Then he heard Vader and Moeder talk softly in the hall and suddenly he thought of Ruth again.

"Is Ruth very sick?" he asked.

"She is much better now," Werner said. "And she'll surely be altogether better soon. Just wait, at Easter she'll be able to go egg-hunting again."

Gees came to say it was time for lunch.

She served lunch only for Werner and Pieter Pim on a corner of the table, and she tied Pieter's bib on so roughly that he couldn't help sticking his tongue out at her when she turned her back.

Even Gees wasn't her old self. Nor were the children. Jan and Jaap came home from school at an unusually early time, both perspiring from pedalling so hard against the wind. It was real Dutch weather—rainy and stormy; now and then hail-showers. Moeder sat down behind the tea-tray. She had an encouraging smile for the dejected faces around the table.

"Ruth," she said, "Ruth talks about ribbons all the time. Does anybody know what she means?"

"Me," said Pieter Pim with a big piece of toast in his cheek. "I know about the ribbons." He chewed and swallowed to empty his mouth. "Ruth bought ribbons from juffrouw Schevedeur that time when she was so mad at me, near the railroad crossing, before Elly's party." It was a confused story, but Moeder seemed to understand it very well. Pieter Pim felt very important, when she went on asking, "Did she bring the ribbons home, Pieter?"

"She must have. She bought them, but it took so long and we had to go home for supper, and she said that I could go on and then I waited for her at the crossing and then she started to cry. . . ."

"We know that by now," Jaap grumbled.

But Moeder said that Pieter had remembered it all very well, and that he could now take a little walk with her in the garden. She needed some fresh air.

"It's rotten weather, Moeder," Jan warned.

"Never mind, I'll put on my cape."

Pieter Pim held Moeder's hand, and walked with her along the rose-path to the gate. He told her how he had helped Werner with his homework, but Moeder didn't seem to listen. She was looking out over the heath where somebody was approaching, somebody carrying a suitcase and struggling against the wind. Then Moeder let go of Pieter's hand, and began to run. Fancy, Moeder ran out of the gate and up the heath, to meet somebody who was coming! And that somebody was Miep. She threw her arms around Moeder, and to Pieter's great amazement they remained standing there in the wind and the rain. Pieter Pim got a lump in his throat and his eyes stung, because after all it was wonderful that Moeder and Miep loved each other so much, even in the rain.

Slowly the days passed. In the sick-room Ruth's small body was lying motionless and Moeder and Adelheid took turns in nursing.

"They say all those things about Germans," Moeder said to Miep, "but look at her devotion and love. Nothing is too much for her."

"Yes," Miep said, "that's what's so stupid about people. Because the Nazis are bad, all Germans are bad. As if Adelheid is responsible for what Hitler is doing. But most people can't see beyond their own noses."

"Mother had a lot to say about my taking a German girl into the house. Mother ignored her at Christmas, remember?"

"You should hear Oma these days. She says that you should come and live in Amsterdam behind the Waterlinie. There you are safe, she says. That's the general idea. There are people from the Eastern provinces who have rented apartments in Amsterdam so that if needed they can escape to them."

"What a waste of money," Moeder sighed.

Yes, Adelheid ran upstairs, downstairs, and nursed Ruth as she were her own sister. She got paler every day, her eyes were red-rimmed with fatigue, but she was always ready, and often sent Moeder to her bedroom to have a little rest or to find some comfort with little Anne. Anne, who grew like a weed and was unaware of all the trouble around her, had a smile for everyone in the family.

Vader now visited his patients again. Miep had gone back to Amsterdam. Pieter Pimple's mother had taken pity on Pieter Pim. Now he often went there to play and, when Pieter Pimple was at school, Pieter Pim drove with Hein Uienkruier, or Vader would take him along, up the heath.

There was still a different atmosphere in the house. They only whispered. They stole on the tiptoe past Ruth's room and listened at the door for a sign of improvement. Jan especially took it very much to heart. Only now did he realize how sweet Ruth had been to him, how she had helped him, always patient, and how he had really relied on her help.—If she gets better, Jan thought, and he made all kinds of promises. If she gets better, I'll resign from the Boy Scouts, then I'll even work Sundays . . . if she gets better, I'll take her to school every morning on the back of my bicycle . . .

if she gets better, I'll never growl at her again, I'll never tease her again. . . .

The strange thing was that Jan, in spite of his good intentions, couldn't work at all. He sat in his room and listened with ears cocked to every noise from Ruth's room. He couldn't keep his attention on his homework and his task. It was just the time of the exams for the Easter report. The average mark of the past three months was added to the marks you got with your exams, and that decided your report mark. He had already flunked geometry, French had only been so-so, and in a few days they were going to have the German exam.

Finally one night the children in turns were allowed to say hello to Ruth. Very quietly they slipped into her little room and nodded hello to her. "Hello, Ruth, how are you feeling now?"

It was a strange Ruth, her curls cut, her eyes twice as big as usual in a thin, pale face. Oh, how Ruth had changed! You always could read everything she thought and felt in Ruth's eyes. And now . . . they looked so dull and tired. As though she didn't care to see her brothers.

She smiled faintly for a moment when Werner took her hand lying on the sheet, and kissed it. Then, without any warning at all she fell asleep again.

Before going to bed Moeder and Jaap took a walk up

the heath. It was a glorious spring night, clear under the light of moon and stars.

"Ruth isn't making much headway yet," Jaap said. It was really a question for he hoped to get a reassuring answer from Moeder.

"Physically she's really all right again. Vader says it's a question of time. I've got the feeling that there's something else at the back of it. She's worrying about something. When she was still very ill she kept talking about ribbons and about a certain Elly. Yesterday she asked me if, when she's better, she'll have to go back to school right away. . . . When I said that it would probably be another few weeks, she was a little relieved."

"Why don't you go to school and try to find out what happened?"

Moeder laughed. "I needn't even try; there's so much among children of which teachers and parents know nothing. Small incidents, difficulties. As a mother you often have to guess. Jaap, you know that. You never came to me when you were in trouble. Jan is different. When he's in the dumps you notice it and sooner or later he comes out with it. But you are different and Ruth, too, swallows a lot of things, even though she's so much younger."

Moeder had given Jaap an arm and they walked on like that for a while. The heath path was a white line in the moonlight. Now and then the wind sent shreds of sound from the village towards them. There the spring fair was in full swing, some shaky booths, a fritter-booth, a merry-go-round, and a wobbly roller coaster. There the village's young people enjoyed themselves. To go to the real Fair, people crossed the Rijn and the Waal, to go to Nijmegen.

"Tomorrow Easter vacation starts," Jaap reminded Moeder.

"I'm curious about your report card," Moeder gave his arm a little pinch. "How did you do?"

"Not badly. You know, Moeder, there's one thing I hope and that is that the principal won't make his usual speech tomorrow when he hands out the reports. That silly talk . . . the future belongs to youth . . . hard times, but it's up to you. . . . We know that by now . . . . The future belongs to youth, indeed! Moeder, they say it, but what do they *do* about it? Ever since I can remember, or at least ever since I've been conscious of things, we've heard about war. There'll be war, there'll be war. Why do the grown-ups always make speeches to us? Let them try instead to make the world a better place."

"But you've got your music, haven't you, Jaap; nobody can take that away from you? You can make the world a better place with your music. You can make the people feel that there are other things besides fighting and hating. That is your mission, Jaap. Every child can do his bit to make the world a better place. Every single child in his own way."

Jaap hooked his arm into Moeder's and silently they walked towards the house.

"I'm going to do all kinds of things in the Easter vacation," Jaap told her. "I'm going to the Fair in Nijmegen, and if you don't mind I'm going to take a bicycle trip to the bulb fields and then on to The Hague to see the Peace Palace and the *Mauritshuis* and those old government buildings. I'm going with a girl from my class and we'll sleep in youth hostels along the way. There are big ones which have sections for girls and boys."

Chapter 12

EASTER HOLIDAYS

JAN AND JAAP were bicycling home. Jan was annoyed. He had his hands in his pockets. True, his Easter report was much better than the one at Christmas, but still not good enough to go on to the next class.

"Come on, hold on to your handle-bar; you'll break your neck," Jaap grumbled. "I don't care so much about you, but I do about my bike. If you knock me down, I won't be able to leave tomorrow."

For a while they rode on silently. The sun shone stronger every day, that is, whenever it got a chance to shine—for, oh, it rained so much in spring. Jan wriggled comfortably, but, of course, his handle-bar tipped around, and he landed in the ditch beside the road. Jaap waited till he had scrambled up. Anyone else would have gone on, Jan thought. But not Jaap. He was different in everything, Jan decided. Tomorrow he was going on a bicycling trip with a girl. Other boys didn't do that. They went with a whole bunch and made a lot of noise. The girl was different, too. Very independent and quiet. Jan felt shy in her company.

"Will you send me a card on the way?" Jan asked.

"Gosh, no," Jaap said, "I've got other things to do. And anyway, you're going on a bicycle trip yourself."

"Why, that will be right near home. Through the blossoming *Betuwe*. That's two hours biking to the South. And now that so much land has been flooded to keep the enemy out, there'll be a lot less flowering fruit trees than other years."

"The cherry orchard of Bunnik," Jaap reminded him. That cherry orchard belonged to a former school friend of Vader's. They went there when the trees were flowering, and later, in July, they crossed the Rhine to eat cherries there. They picked handfuls of them from the trees. Nowhere in the world were cherries as good as in Holland. Warm-red, juicy and sweet.

"I wouldn't mind eating some now," Jaap smacked his lips.

"May I borrow your hockey-stick during vacation?" Jan asked before they went through the gate. "Mine has got all warped this winter."

"You may keep it; I won't play any more."

"You're getting to be a real bore," Jan said ungratefully.

Jaap gave him a big push, which sent Jan sprawling on the lawn, with his bicycle on top of him.

They went into the house, still fooling with each other.

"Oh please, boys. Stop the racket," begged Moeder, who was coming down the stairs with her arms full of linen. "I'm so terribly busy. Everything's going wrong. Adelheid has suddenly disappeared. I have to take Ruth to Noordwijk tomorrow and I haven't half packed yet."

In the living room there was an awful to-do. Pieter Pim was making a Palm-Easter branch. His tongue was hanging from his mouth with the effort. On Palm Sunday there would be a procession of children. It was an old Dutch custom. Moeder warned him that he had started too early, the branches would dry out. And the little *koek* rooster on top was getting hard, but once Pieter got something into his head there was no joking about it. He had decided to outdo all the children with his Palm-Easter branch.

At the table Miss Tonia the seamstress who, ever since they could remember, came once a week to mend, was ripping a seam.

On the veranda Gees was beating out blankets.

The radio was playing a gay waltz. And in the midst of all that noise Anne sat is her play-pen, talking contentedly to herself and expertly dissecting a little toy.

"Jan, will you put on some water for the tea?" Moeder asked. "Yes, Adelheid suddenly left. Back to Germany. Now do you understand that, Jaap? She was so satisfied here. Such a nice girl, to let me down just like that. A note in her room and all her things gone. She just left quietly."

"I think that Mr. Hitler could give you the answer to that," Jaap said.

"I called up the 'Mädchenverrein.' They couldn't give me any information."

"Yeah . . ." Jaap said. He didn't know what to say. It was a bad sign that Adelheid suddenly wanted to go back to Germany. Moeder was so naïve in that respect.

Miss Tonia put the linen under the sewing machine and Jaap started turning the handle for her. No, Toon, as the children called her, didn't want an electric sewing machine, not even one with a pedal. She'd rather hold on to the old things.

Jan dawdled around a little in the room, and then he went slowly upstairs to Ruth. She was waiting for him in the little easy chair that Vader and Moeder had given her after her illness.

"Oh Jan, show it to me quick. I'm so curious to see how it is."

"How what is? . . ." Jan asked.

"Please Jan, don't be silly. Your report, of course."

"Oh that . . . that's somewhere downstairs."

Ruth looked at him with so much indignation in her dark eyes, that he left the room to get the report book. While he went slowly downstairs, he cursed himself for dancing to Ruth's tune, but when he came up later with his school-bag he hated himself. During Ruth's illness he had promised himself that he would do everything for her if she would get better and now that she was better, he teased her. Ruth would be disappointed by his marks. She would say,—Oh, Jan, what a pity . . . why didn't you work harder?

Oh, darn that school!

But Ruth didn't show her disappointment. "You'll make it all right," she said.

In the living room Moeder was standing at the telephone. Miss Tonia had a finger against her lips. "It's Amsterdam. Miep is on the 'phone."

"But Miep, what nonsense," Moeder was saying. "And if anything happens, I can come and get Ruth in a few hours, can't I? No, I don't agree with you. . . .

Yes, all right. . . . I'll talk it over with Vader. . . . 'Bye . . ."

Moeder was looking worried as she put the telephone back and she was very absent-minded while she poured the tea.

"Well, this is the last time I shall be drinking tea with you," Ruth said.

"For the time being, you should say," Miss Tonia corrected. "And I wouldn't sigh like that. Lots of people would like to change places with you. My dear, think of it, six lovely weeks at the sea side."

"Would you like to go, Toon?" Ruth asked.

"Of course, my dear. I've never been at the sea shore."

"Oh, Moekie, can Toon come along for the ride, tomorrow?" Ruth begged.

"If Vader can spare the car, it's all right."

Luckily Vader happened to come in at that moment and they could ask him immediately.

"It's all right," said Vader. "I won't have any distant visits. I'll take Jan's bicycle. Moeder can drive you up."

"Aren't you happy, Toon?" Ruth asked, and, without waiting for an answer, she said, "I'm awfully happy. Now I like going much better."

"Miep called up," Moeder told Vader. "She says that it is irresponsible to send Ruth away now. She says that we should stay together. If there is an invasion we won't be able to reach Ruth."

"Oh, come now," Vader said impatiently. "Miep

lets herself get all upset, there in Amsterdam. The Germans will know better than that." And to the children, "You'd better show me your report cards. I'm curious about your marks. Did they send you a report too, Ruth?"

But before Ruth could answer Moeder said, "Adelheid has gone."

"How do you mean 'gone?' " Vader looked around the room as if he thought the German girl was hiding somewhere.

Ruth laughed.

"It's hardly a laughing matter," Jaap warned gloomily.

"Now what exactly is the trouble?" Vader asked impatiently.

"Adelheid ran away. She packed her things and disappeared. She left a note saying she was going back to Germany."

"What about the air-raid shelters, Vader?" Jaap asked, jokingly.

But Vader didn't seem to be in the mood for jokes. "That's crude sarcasm, Jaap."

Jaap's face became scarlet.

"You know very well," Vader continued, "that there's no sense building air-raid shelters in a village of less than ten thousand people. There's no factory or depot near here, and so there's no reason whatsoever for bombing our village. What had to be done has been taken care of. We're protected by the Water-linie."

Moeder had poured a cup of tea. "Here, Vader," she said, "here's some tea. Sit down. You must be tired."

But Vader was seriously annoyed, and Moeder's attempts to distract him were of no avail. He took the cup of tea, and the reports, and went to his consulting-room.

The family stayed behind in a depressed mood. Vader didn't usually get cross. They felt that there was more behind his annoyance than Jaap's sarcastic remark.

"You'd better go and see Vader," Moeder whispered to him after a while.

That was just what Jaap wanted.

"It was really disgusting of me, Vader," he said as he entered the consulting-room.

"You understand, don't you, my boy, that we've done everything that is necessary. The large cities, like Amsterdam and Rotterdam need shelters but there's no danger of bombardments in a village like ours. Anyway, as I told you before, we're protected by the Water-linie. We're strong, and the Germans know it. You prove, by your remark, that you didn't think about it sufficiently. You're letting yourself be carried away by the war psychosis like so many people. That's just what the Germans want. They want to break our morale because our neutrality is worrying them. People like Miep cause a panic. We stand firm, and will resolutely wait for what will happen. Do you understand, Jaap?

Jaap traced the pattern of the rug with his foot. He

didn't look up. "I don't know, Vader. So terribly much has happened already. And you should hear the N.S.B. members at my school talk, that fellow Hafkenscheid, for instance."

"Oh well, son, the National Socialists in our country have no importance at all. With a leader like Mussert they'll never amount to anything. You don't hear much from them any more. Sometimes they make a little noise in the *Tweede Kamer* meetings. . . . Don't let yourself be led astray by the tall talk of a few boys at school. When you go biking tomorrow, have a good look at our defenses. They'll give you confidence. . . ."

On his bicycle trip through Holland Jaap indeed saw quite a lot of the defenses. Flooded land, tank barricades, guarded bridges, and closed roads. The things of which they had only talked till now suddenly became real. So much so that he and Bep enjoyed the trip less than they had thought they would.

But they didn't talk about it, they kept their thoughts to themselves. Even later when they stood in front of the *Vredespaleis*, "The Peace Palace," in The Hague they didn't discuss it. Nevertheless they were both thinking the same thing. It had been built before the World War from funds contributed by an American, Andrew Carnegie. Each country had contributed to the building. Everything, from the hand-wrought gate to the precious art objects inside, had been a series of gifts from the member states of the international Peace Conference of 1907. But it had hardly been completed when the World War broke out. And there it stood—"The Peace Palace"—in the midst of a world full of hate and struggle.

Much later that day, as they sat on the grounds of the youth-hostel, looking at the sunset, Jaap said, "You see, Bep, they built a *Vredespaleis* to show that mankind has at last found the true confederacy. But inside, in their hearts, they were not ready for it. Inside they felt hate and greed and lust for power. That's it, you see. As long as people don't change within themselves, the world won't change. It begins with every individual. A feeling of friendship for your neighbor."

"But there are people who have that feeling, Jaap," Bep said, "like you and me, for instance."

"Sure," said Jaap, "there might be ninety-nine people who feel like that, but if the hundredth is different, then it's no good. Most people don't want war, but they're not sufficiently strong in their convictions to oppose it."

"That day will come, Jaap, after this war, perhaps," Bep comforted him.

"Well, I hope so." Jaap looked at the setting sun that bathed the whole landscape in a red glow. "I hope it will happen some day."

Chapter 13

WAR

THE SPRING was cold and wet, as it usually is in the low lands. The clouds chased along the grey sky, and the people stood at their windows and looked anxiously at the buds on the trees. The wind was merciless.

Then summer came. Big majestic clouds in a clear blue sky. Summer days were feast-days in Holland.

There weren't many of them, and people were as grateful for each sunny hour as for a beautiful gift.

Moeder thought of how happy Ruth would be in this fine weather. She would enjoy herself at the beach. And she would be home on the tenth of May, quite the old Ruth again. That was already apparent from her letters.

Warm, spontaneous Ruth, home again! Moeder looked forward to it. She had re-decorated Ruth's room. A surprise . . . but also because time went faster doing that kind of work. They had painted the walls light yellow, hung new blue curtains, and dyed the couch-cover. Jan had built a little table, and stained the other furniture. Pieter Pim, who now went to kindergarten, had colored a picture, to hang on the wall.

Yes, indeed, Pieter Pim went to school. If you wanted to, you could learn to read there. And Pieter wouldn't have been Pieter if he hadn't taken advantage of the opportunity. Preferably he read billboards and posters, so everybody at home was informed of all that occurred in the village. Blackout regulations . . . the request to turn in horses . . .

Luckily Gezina was allowed to keep drawing the greengrocer's cart. Uienkruier and Pieter had worried about that.

"You see, Pieter, if I have to give up Gezina, I'm out of business," Uienkruier said. But Pieter assured him that it certainly would not happen . . . and in case the misfortune did befall him, Pieter Pim would see to it that Uienkruier could borrow the doctor's car. You bet he would. The greengrocer scratched his ear; he didn't believe that so readily.

Miep came home often. Since Maarten had been called into the Army, she was lonely in Amsterdam, and spent a great part of her monthly allowance on train fare.

But when she came home there sometimes was friction. About the radio, for example. Jaap liked to listen to concerts, Jan preferred jazz music, and Miep wanted to hear all the news reports. She was very much excited about the progress of the war and talked continuously about spies and fifth columnists on the home front.

"War hysteria," Jan said with contempt.

Vader didn't like the children to use expressions the full meaning of which they didn't understand. "Where did you get that piece of wisdom?"

"School," said Jan.

Vader couldn't say much to that.

"Go ahead, laugh at me," Miep said. "You'll talk differently some day."

She now was an ambulance driver. Some time ago Maarten had taught her to drive. Exercises were being held. When Miep told about it, the children hung on her words.

Jan would have loved to do something of the same kind, but he didn't even have time for the scout work.

He was boning. At last it had become much easier for him than it used to be. When Ruth came home he would surprise her with a couple of beautiful marks. How it would make her sit up!

May 12th was Moeder's birthday. "Despite the present circumstances," as Vader put it, they would have a garden party. They would hang Chinese lanterns, which later on they would carry in their hands when they took a walk on the dark heath.

"Do you think we'll be allowed to walk over the heath with lights?" Pieter Pim asked. "Maybe they'll think we're spies."

"Children, please stop talking about spies and traitors. I don't hear anything else from you these days. It's bad enough that the grownups talk about it all day and suspect everybody; if the children start it, too, that's the last straw. From now on any one who mentions such things must pay a one cent fine."

"Then you'd better ask Miep for a guilder," Jaap said. "She'll be your best customer."

But that same night the prohibition was repealed by Moeder, for the radio broadcasted news about the arrest of real traitors. And now Moeder was talking about it herself.

"Shouldn't we let Ruth come home immediately?" she asked Vader. "She can catch the train tomorrow morning if we call her now."

"Come now, Moeder," Vader reassured her, "don't

lose your head. Ruth can stay in Noordwijk for the few remaining days."

Moeder didn't say much to that. She could see that Vader wasn't calm any more either, although he knew how to control himself.

A few days later Vader called Werner in his room. "My boy, I've thought it over seriously and I think you should go to America. You'd better be on the safe side."

"Do you think there'll be an invasion?"

"I don't know what's going to happen, Werner, but we have to face all possibilities. If the Germans come they're sure to pick up the German refugees first. It's because we are so fond of you that we want you to be safe. I'll write to the American consul." Vader patted Werner's shoulder encouragingly but he himself was distressed about it. Werner looked so deeply disappointed.

Moeder found him later on the heath, where she went to gather flowers.

"It'll be another few weeks before you'll get your papers," she reassured him, "and you'll see how interesting you'll find America. You know, it's always been a dream of mine to see it. Some skyscrapers in New York are fifty stories high. Just think . . . the only skyscraper in Amsterdam has only eight stories. Don't be so gloomy. Maybe you won't even want to leave there."

Werner didn't answer. He couldn't be consoled.

Silently they walked home. It was such a beautiful

summer night. The air smelled good and everything seemed so peaceful.

They put the flowers in a pail of water, so they would be fresh the next morning when Ruth arrived, and before they went to bed they hung in the hall the sign on which Jan had painted, "Welcome Home, Ruth."

"Thank God, she'll be home tomorrow," Moeder said before she put out the light. "Tomorrow all my little lambs will be home again. I really didn't feel easy about her."

But Moeder still didn't feel easy. She couldn't go to sleep, and lay wide awake, staring out of the window into the moonlit sky.

Later she slipped out of the bedroom and went into the children's rooms.

Anne, having kicked the bedclothes off, was sleeping on her tummy, and didn't even wake up when Moeder tucked her in. Pieter Pim, lying across his bed with his hair stuck to his forehead, had apparently fallen asleep while playing with a litle toy train. He was lying right on top of it, but it didn't seem to bother hm.

Werner was tossing about restlessly. He seemed to be having a nightmare. Moeder talked soothingly to him for a moment. He went on sleeping quietly after that. She also looked in on Jan and Jaap.

"Where have you been?" asked Vader, who woke up when she returned to the bedroom.

"I had to see that everything was all right," she said.

Toward morning she awoke with a start. She heard a noise she couldn't identify. One moment it was clear, then again it seemed to sink away into the silence of the morning. Later she realized that she had heard planes, droning high above the heath.

She heard the soft slap of bare feet on the linoleum in Jan's room, and upstairs, Gees was getting up.

Jan was standing on the balcony outside his room, and tried, in the twilight, to find the planes that were flying somewhere high up in the sky. But it was still too dark.

"Jan, what are you doing there?" whispered Vader, who had awakened. "You'll catch a cold; come in quickly."

"Planes, Vader," Jan said nervously.

"They're probably practicing. Now come in, my boy."

But Jan didn't come in. These weren't manœuvres. Planes in formation were flying high above the clouds.

"Come on downstairs, Vader," whispered Jan. "The radio."

They waited impatiently till the tubes warmed up. But the radio was silent, like other nights; no station was broadcasting.

"I can't understand it," Jan said.

"How many planes do you think went over?"

"Fifty."

"Well, let's go to bed," Vader said soberly. "They must have been exercises. There are so many night flights these days."

About an hour later the telephone near Vader's bed rang. It was the mayor's voice. "Doctor," he said, "it's happened. The Germans have invaded our country. Can you come here immediately?"

While Vader dressed hurriedly, Moeder went downstairs to make a cup of tea for him. There she found the three boys, Werner, Jan and Jaap, bent over the radio. So Jan hadn't gone back to bed, but had returned to the radio. Later he had apparently called the other boys.

It was evident that the broadcaster was excited. In a scarcely controlled voice he kept repeating the same summons: the reserve-troops must report immediately.

Vader stood drinking the tea that Moeder had prepared for him.

"Listen, boys," he said, "I'll do my best to get back home as soon as possible, but I'm afraid it won't be before this afternoon. So, mind you, you're Moeder's only support. Try and help her as much as possible. Stay calm and firm. . . ."

Moeder accompanied Vader to the garage. "Ruth," she said, "and Miep . . . "

"I'll do what I can," Vader promised. "I'll phone Noordwijk; you try to get in touch with Miep. If they're going to bomb us, which I don't believe, but if they do, then go up the heath with the children and hide against a slope or in a hole."

Upstairs Pieter Pim appeared on the balcony. "Vader . . . Vader . . . Gees says that the Germans have invaded us. . . . Is that true, Vader? And where are you going? Are you going to buy a gun? Buy one for me, too, Vader. . . . " he called excitedly.

"I'm going to my patients," Vader said quietly. "You'd better get dressed quickly."

Pieter Pim wanted to ask a lot more, but Gees grasped the collar of his pajamas and drew him inside.

"Now what shall we do with Werner?" Moeder asked.

"Don't worry. They're not here yet. The English will be here any moment to help us. They won't get us so easily. Keep Werner with you, and pack a suitcase with his things in case the worst happens."

Later Vader called from the village. "Have Jaap come as quickly as possible. There's work to be done."

"How is everything?" Moeder asked.

"I don't know any more than you do."

"They say that they are letting parachutists down."

"Yes," said Vader.

"And violent fights at the airports."

"Courage," Vader consoled her, "they won't get us."

Jaap jumped on his bicycle, and raced away, stared after by Jan, who would have loved to go with him.

But Moeder said that he was the eldest now and that she couldn't possibly spare him.

Werner just sat at the radio and continuously tuned in to the German stations, too. But these didn't broadcast anything about the invasion.

The telephone wasn't quiet a moment. Everybody wanted to speak to the doctor. To many people he was the support and consultant in all troubles. Now, too, people expected a comforting word from him.

"How is it possible . . . " they said to Moeder. For more than a century Holland had lived in peace, people had no war experience. They couldn't grasp it. Moeder consoled them as best she could. So many people had sons and brothers in the army.

Jan kept running outside all the time to look at the planes that flew over.

In the South and the North heavy fighting was going on, but here life went on as usual. On the outside, at least, people tried to go about their business as if they felt perfectly calm.

About noon Uienkruier came by. The baker and the milkman had been around already.

"What a mess, Pieter, what a mess," Uienkruier said when Pieter helped him weigh the carrots. Gees had said that he could choose the vegetables, and of course he took what he liked best. Germans or no Germans. . . . Gees said that she herself didn't know what she was doing. "My old mother lives in Brabant, right on the German border, and she's all alone," she repeated over and over again.

Pieter Pim made himself very useful all morning. He was allowed to give Anne her porridge, because Moeder was too busy. Of course, she showed him how to do it first.

"You needn't be afraid at all, as long as I am around," Pieter said. "I'll just tell the Germans that you are our mother, and then they won't do anything to you."

"That'll be a help," Jan said sarcastically. But Moeder gave him a sign.

Moeder tried continuously to reach Miep. But the line was blocked, and the operator asked her not to make more calls than was strictly necessary.

Just after lunch the planes started to come over again. Some of them flew on, but others circled over the heath and flew in the direction of the village, where the siren was screaming.

Moeder, Gees, and the children, standing by the window, saw the bombs fall. They seemed so harmless. Small black tubes. But flames shot into the air, followed by the sound of explosions.

"Good Lord," Gees said. "Good Lord." She had put her arms around Moeder and the children. Nobody said another word. When the planes had gone, they noticed that they had all been holding each other tightly.

After the all-clear signal Vader telephoned again.

He asked Moeder to prepare beds for the wounded.

And then they didn't have any more time to think of their own safety. They only paid attention to the people who had to be cared for. Even when in the evening three Germans planes paid a visit to the village again, and razed the station to the ground, they stuck to their posts with the patients. They talked to them, repeated the encouraging words of the Queen, who had talked over the radio that morning.

There was juffrouw Mes of the candy shop, who had been taken from beneath the rubble of her store with a broken leg. One whole family, father, mother, and two children who lived across the station, badly battered and frightened. The wife of the station master, for whom Vader had but little hope left, and a boy who was unconscious, and whose name they didn't know.

The district nurse had come with them so these people could get expert treatment. Later in the evening Bep, Jaap's friend, came to help. Jaap was going to spend the night in the village.

"What is Jaap doing in the village?" Jan inquired of Bep.

"Dragging things around," Bep said, "dragging sand-bags, records and papers that have to be brought to safety, rubble and stones when they're looking for victims of the bombing."

"Were there many?"

"No. They only aimed at the station and the railroad, to cut off the communications, but of course they hit the surrounding houses and streets."

"But it isn't an important communication line," Jan said.

"Every little bit helps," Bep said bitterly.

"It was well prepared, wasn't it?"

"Disgustingly well," Bep said. Then she pointed at the sign with "Welcome Home, Ruth," which was still hanging in the hall. "You haven't heard anything yet, have you?"

"Nothing," said Jan, disconsolate. "And she's in such a dangerous spot, there on the coast. If the English start bombing, they have to evacuate that region, and heaven knows what will become of Ruth."

"Awful for your mother," Bep said.

"She is marvelous."

Yes, Moeder really bore up well. She had insisted that they have tea together in the living room as they did on all other nights. She was sitting behind the tea-table, tired, but kind and calm with an interested word for everybody. But the children were very quiet. Pieter Pim had great difficulty in keeping his eyes open. He nibbled sleepily at a cookie and was, perhaps for the first time in his life, docile when Gees offered to put him to bed.

"You helped splendidly, Jan Stavast," Gees praised him.

"Later I'm going to be a soldier, and then I'll shoot all the Huns," Pieter said suddenly. His eyes burned, but his trembling lower lip gave him away.

"You come with me, my little heart," Gees said. She put her arms around him, but Pieter pulled himself free. "Say, I'm not a little baby," he said. "I'll shoot all the Huns."

"Don't talk nonsense," Jan said irritably. And when Pieter Pim had left with Gees, he burst out, "Moeder, why do you let him say such things? . . ."

"But I don't let him say such things, Jan. Children repeat what they hear, without thinking about it."

"Oh, it's rotten," Jan said.

"Don't think about it, Jan, in a few weeks the war will be over, and Pieter will forget soon enough."

At that moment the telephone rang. When Moeder picked it up, she heard a young voice, somewhat shy, asking, "Are you Ruth's mother? I am Elly. Would you tell me if Ruth has come home yet?"

"No," Moeder answered, "she hasn't."

"Did you hear from her?"

"No," Moeder said.

Then there was a silence on the other end of the line, in which the girl apparently was making up her mind.

"Is there anything else you wanted to know?" Moeder asked kindly.

"I wish," the girl said hesitantly, "I wish I could do something for you. Something that would make you forget that Ruth isn't with you."

"Well . . . " Moeder said, "I don't think there is anything that could make me forget that."

"Couldn't I help you?" Elly asked. "Wouldn't you let me take Ruth's place? She would help you with the wounded in your house. My mother told me you are nursing them all yourself. Maybe I can come over and help you. Please let me . . . won't you? . . ."

And, as Moeder knew something had happened between Ruth and Elly, she decided, "Yes, you may come tomorrow morning. Ruth will be very pleased if she hears of your offer, I am sure."

"I will work very hard," the girl said, "and do everything you'll ask me to. Do you think Ruth will come home soon?"

"I don't think she can now."

"I am sure she's all right," the girl said.

When Moeder put down the receiver the siren in the village began screaming again. In the silence it sounded like the anguished crying of a child. Gees came down with Anne on her arm, holding Pieter by the hand. Moeder and Bep went upstairs to the patients. Werner and Jan stood by the window in the hall, looking out over the heath. On the other side was the village, dead, without a single light; only on the right, where the station was, the fire of the bombardment was still smouldering.

They listened intently to every sound from outside. They heard the familiar droning of planes, which now assumed such a frightful meaning. This time they passed over to do their work of destruction elsewhere.

From upstairs came the crying of a child, and the reassuring voice of Moeder.

Jan and Werner didn't sleep much that night. The excitement kept them awake. Moreover, it was very noisy in the house, with the patients to be cared for. Even the silence on the heath was disturbed. Planes kept flying over, and, from the village, where the fire had now been put out, came the screaming of the siren. Just after midnight a long column of cars rumbled by over the heath road.

At about four o'clock Vader and Jaap returned home. The district nurse drove away on her motor-bicycle, with Bep at the back. It was strange when you came to think of it, that people drove over the heath, just like that, without any protection. Parachutists were landing everywhere in the country, and of course Dutch soldiers were on the look-out . . . but nobody seemed to be afraid. People were too preoccupied with the danger to their country, to dwell on the thought of personal risks. Everybody went straight ahead on the road where his duty lay, soldiers in civilian clothes. . . .

Jaap sat on the edge of his bed. Jan who had given up his room for the wounded, was sitting at the foot of Werner's bed. They looked expectantly at Jaap, but Jaap sat bent forward, with his hands folded between his knees, without saying a word.

"You must be dead," Jan said.

Jaap shrugged his shoulders.

"Do you want something to eat?" Jan tried.

Jaap shook his head. "I'm going to sleep," he said, and slowly started to undress. Werner and Jan silently looked on as Jaap washed himself a little and put on his pajamas.

"Listen, Werner," Jaap started then, "if you're sensible you'll clear out of here."

"Where to?" Werner asked.

"To England," Jaap said.

"You're crazy," Jan exploded.

Jaap turned around with a jerk. "What do you know about it? . . . If you would have seen what I saw, you would talk differently. Those parachutists are coming down everywhere, even in the village. In the Eastern part of the country they wear Dutch uniforms and attack our soldiers in the rear. That's how they take the bridges. If it goes on like that . . ."

"There's the pessimist again," Jan said. "All right, maybe they'll get our bridges and airports, but think of all the land which has been flooded. How can they get through that? Surely not with parachutists . . ."

"If they drop enough of them behind the Inundated Belt."

Jan pulled the blanket over his head. "I'm going to sleep," he muttered.

But he couldn't sleep. He was too excited. It seemed as if his blood was rushing through him with abnormal speed. Thoughts kept buzzing in his head. Pictures of what he had actually seen, or only heard on the radio or imagined, kept changing in front of his closed eyes: Parachutists floating down under the dome-shaped white roof. Disentangling themselves, they set up machine-guns or sneaked to a hiding place. Some never got up after they landed because the Dutch soldiers were on the alert. But more and more parachutists came, just as the radio had said. They dropped out of the sky like leaves off a tree in the wind. They wore Dutch uniforms . . . soldiers, conductors, guards . . . others were disguised as Dutch priests or women. They attacked the defenders from behind and acted as guides for the German troops. Like mosquitoes on a hot evening, they swarmed and attacked. They sneaked through cracks towards the light. When you destroyed them, more came, and more and more.

Seaplanes . . . burning hangars . . . people looking for a place to hide . . . Miep driving her ambulance on the crowded roads . . . a plane shot down in the streets in The Hague, its passengers, a German general and his horse all dressed up for the victorious entry in the residential town . . . Ruth dragging her suitcases along the road, people in shelters . . . Vader operating on a wounded woman in the barn . . . Pieter Pim very pale, shouting at the planes . . . a child crying over the noise of the bombardment . . . soldiers shooting at the Germans who tried to cross the Inundated Belt in rubber boats . . . It all flashed behind his closed eyelids, like a newsreel. . . .

And asleep, too, these pictures kept coming in dreams . . . even more confused . . . till he was again wakened by the noise on the road. Columns passed, choosing this back way to the frontier; Dutch planes roared past, messengers on motorcycles tore by with terrific speed.

When morning came, Jan slept without dreams, but then he was aroused again by the creaking of the garage door; Vader was leaving.

Jan went on the balcony. "May I go with you, Vader? . . ."

Vader hesitated. "Well, all right, but when Jaap arrives at nine, you must go back to Moeder."

On the road to the village they passed trucks loaded with soldiers, who looked with watchful eyes at the sky. They were going towards the German border. Young soldiers all, the last conscripted. Jan felt pity and envy at the same time. Vader was stopped several times, and had to show his papers. But then he could pass.

"Good luck, doctor," the guards said, "good luck to you! They'll need you."

In the village there was still a smell of fire. Many villagers had parked their cars in front of their house and were busy loading their most precious belongings. They kept running to and fro, time and again scanning the sky for the dreaded planes. They had decided to flee to the West or to Belgium. Neighbors tried to persuade them to stay. "No sense in moving," they would say. But the people who had made up their minds wouldn't listen, although they stretched the hour of departure by carrying more to their cars. The Nazis were machine-gunning people on the roads, as they had done in Norway and Poland. The radio had told about it. It was true. So maybe it would be better to stay home. But time moved so slowly and there was so little to do. To keep active, to keep busy, they just loaded their cars up.

At the town hall a big crowd had gathered. The doctor couldn't pass. "What's going on?" he asked. One of the farmers stuck his head in the car. "They got a fifth columnist," he said in a whisper. "It's Hafkenscheid's son," he added. "Can you believe such a thing, doctor? A mere boy of sixteen years . . . if it were my son . . ." he stopped talking, looking at Jan, who listened.

"Hafkenscheid is in Jaap's grade," Jan said excitedly.

But the doctor started the car, blowing his horn so people would make room for them. "He will be taken care of," he said. Jan didn't dare to ask again. Vader looked very upset, muttering to himself and shaking his head. "What a world, what a world . . . children, too . . ."

Indeed, children, too, were involved in those horrible, incredible happenings, but not like this boy. The other children, and probably all over the country, did their utmost to lighten the burden of the grownups. At home Elly worked. Up and down the stairs she went, never tiring. She followed the given instructions as well as she could and carried on all those duties, small in themselves, but which made the suffering of the wounded so much more easy to bear.

And Moeder, watching her, didn't ask any questions. She understood that Elly in her own small way was making up for something she knew she had done wrong. She didn't ask her to leave, she let her share and treated her just as she would have treated Ruth. She called Elly's mother several times during the day to reassure her about her daughter.

That day seemed endless, and the next too. As the planes came back and the parachutists landed by the thousands behind the Inundated Belt, more people decided to flee. The war came nearer. Now the house wasn't safe any more, the home where they had been born, where they had lived all their lives. As if the roof had been blown off. And the streets they knew so well weren't safe either. Around every corner danger lurked. The village had become alien, so the people thought, they might as well move somewhere else.

Even the Queen was gone; she had fled to England. The members of the House of Orange, Queen Wilhelmina, Princess Juliana and her children were in London. Also the government. That was strange, some people thought, till they understood that it was done to safeguard the royal house.

On the fourth night a bomb destroyed the barn, Vader's Laboratory. What had the Germans been looking for? . . . Amidst his worries and sorrow, while he was extinguishing the fire with the garden hose, Vader had to laugh. He laughed . . . Moeder and the boys in their nightclothes, who were beating at the flames in the garden, looked up when Vader laughed. They looked at each other and then they, too, laughed. What were the Germans looking for, when they bombed Vader's primitive Laboratory? . . . They laughed and laughed . . . till all of a sudden Moeder turned around and rushed into the house, crying. . . .

It was almost morning when somebody outside the gate blew the horn of a car.

By now the boys knew that they couldn't go out

on the balcony at night; Vader had forbidden that very strictly. Vader himself did go out and in a loud whisper asked: "Who is it?"

The door of the car was opened. A familiar voice called: "Me, Vader, me . . . Miep . . . Please come down at once. . . .

Vader and Moeder both rushed down, followed by the three boys. In the car at the wheel was Miep, and in the back on the floor, fast asleep, lay Ruth.

"Better get me out first," Miep said. "I hurt my leg, can't walk very well. Don't wake Ruth, she was exhausted and very upset."

"Oh, Miep," Moeder said, the words choking in her throat, "how did you . . . how was it possible . . . this . . . are you wounded? . . ."

"Just a little," Miep said quietly. "A scratch . . . Please, get me out. Let's hurry. I have to get back immediately. Are Werner's things packed? I'll take him to Rotterdam. I put a tourniquet on to stop the bleeding. I can't bend my knee," she explained, when they got her out of the car and helped her to the surgery. While Vader went to work on her leg, Moeder drove the car into the garage, which seemed safer, and with the help of Jaap carried Ruth to her bed, where Elly was fast asleep, exhausted by the work she wasn't accustomed to.

"Thank God, she is safe," Moeder said, "thank God . . ."

When they went down, they met Werner on the stairs. He carried his suitcase and managed to smile at them. Moeder and Jaap both put an arm around his shoulders and so they went down the stairs together.

In the surgery Miep talked to Vader: "They are all over the country . . . trying to get over the Zuiderzeedijk, over the Inundated Belt, advancing from the South. Our boys are marvelous. But we haven't got enough planes left. The airports are gone . . . and in The Hague the fifth columnists shoot from the roofs, they concealed their weapons . . . everything is so confused, but the people are wonderful. There is so much work. I had four hours of sleep altogether. Do you think that Moeder can make me some strong coffee? I'll first get Werner on a boat to England or to the Indies, then I'll sleep. I have been driving since ten o'clock last night, had to get Ruth first."

"How did you get through? . . ." Vader asked, bandaging her leg.

Miep laughed a little. "I don't know," she said. "I was off duty last night to get some sleep for the first time, so I took Maarten's car, and I got through with my papers as an ambulance driver. I don't know how. Some soldiers helped me to get gas. I don't know who shot at the car, the Germans or the Dutch. It happened near Utrecht. Have you seen the holes? They didn't hurt Ruth, though. . . ."

"It was a crazy thing to do," Vader said, but there was no reproach in his voice.

"But you don't know what is going to happen, Vader! This part of the country might get cut off from the West for a long time to come. Nobody knows. . . . Moreover, hundreds of people are moving. Many Jewish people are trying to get out. I think they are right. I'll take Werner. Don't worry. I know how."

Miep drank her black coffee and then went away with Werner. As simple as that. It was just like Miep. . . .

Then on the fourteenth day of May a terrible thing happened. That was the day of Rotterdam. The heart of this industrious city, where thousands of people were crowded together, was raided. That afternoon life seemed to stand still. People all over the country gasped. They looked at each other with a big question in their eyes . . . is this possible, they meant to say . . . is this humanity? . . . Messengers and soldiers passing through the village told about it. One saw the smoke from as far down as the province of Utrecht, they said. Rotterdam burned and almost nine hundred men, women and children perished. . . . Can this be, people thought, while they looked at each other . . . can this be? . . . How will we find the road back to love and friendship after this? . . .

In "The Level Land" nobody spoke because they all knew what the others were thinking about: Where was Miep when it happened? Had Werner boarded a ship, before it happened? Had Miep tried to get some rest in Rotterdam before she returned to her duties in Amsterdam, or had she first driven back to sleep in her own room? This they asked themselves over and over again, and then their thoughts went back to all the inhabitants of Rotterdam, the people they didn't know, but who were their brothers and sisters as well.

Later on that day Holland capitulated. The commander of the army himself broadcasted this decision to the population. The Germans had warned that other cities would suffer the same fate as Rotterdam.

The only one in the room who spoke after the radio went off the air was Pieter Pim. "Can I go to school again?" he asked.

"I guess so," Moeder said in a very strange voice, "I guess you all can go back to school now."

That night when Moeder came to tuck Ruth and Elly in, Ruth whispered: "God will know what Miep has done for me and Werner. He will know that she never did anything wrong. He will watch over her . . . and when He can't guard her, for there are so many people now to look after for Him, you know, Moeder, He will make somebody else watch over her."

When Moeder came back into the parlor, she told what Ruth had said. "Let's believe, like Ruth does," she pleaded. "Let's all be as strong in our belief. We know that it isn't always true. Many people who never harmed anybody have died horribly this afternoon in

Rotterdam. . . . Let's for the moment not think about that . . . for from now on we have to be strong in our faith that what is right survives, and what is wrong will perish. . . . We have to. . . . We lost, the Germans won, but still we are stronger, for we know that we fought to defend ourselves against evil. And we will go on defending ourselves, not with arms, but with the strength of our belief in what's right."

"Isn't that a little childish?" Jaap asked. "You know it, Moeder, the bad aren't always punished nor are the good always saved. . . ."

"That's true, Jaap, I know it. But we have to believe in something to get back on our feet. There is nothing left for us to hold on to, nothing but our own will to survive. If we doubt now, we won't be able to act. Let us just have faith, faith in mankind and righteousness. Let's try it anyway, please, Jaap."

"I'll try," Jaap promised.

"And if . . . if we hear that something has happened . . . to Werner and Miep? . . ." Jan asked.

Mother tried to answer, but she couldn't.

"That should not make any difference," Vader said, while he grasped Moeder's hand on the table. "That's what Moeder meant to say, whatever may happen to them, we will be strong, and so we, and all of us, will survive . . ."

"And now let's go upstairs, to our patients," Moeder said.

Glossary

Achter in the back

Bijenkorf Bee-Hive (name for department store)

Blauw blue

Boterhammen open sandwiches

Concertgebouw municipal concert hall

De Poort van Cleef Port of *Cleve* (town in West Germany), name for restaurant

Gracht canal

Grachten plural of *gracht*

H.B.S. (*Hogere Burger School*) Higher Burgher School, high school

Heer gentleman

IJ river in Holland

Jongejuffrouw young lady

Jordaan name for very old section of Amsterdam

Juffertje abbreviation for *jongejuffrouw;* little miss

Juffrouw woman

Kerstkrans Christmas cake, wreath-shaped

Klompen wooden shoes

Koek spiced cake

Koningin queen

Kwartje twenty-five cents; quarter

Lange Jan Long John (name of church)

Leidsestraat Leidenstreet

Letterbanket almond filled strudel, in the shape of letters

Mädchenverrein society for German girls

Marsepein candy made of ground almonds

Mauritshuis famous museum in the Hague

Meneer sir

Mevrouw madam, ma'am

Moeder mother

Montelbaanstoren name of church tower in Amsterdam

Muisjes sugar-coated anise seeds

M.U.L.O. (*Meer Uitgebreid Lager Onderwijs*) extension of grammar school

Munttoren part of old ramparts and tower of building which used to be the Dutch Mint

N.S.B. Dutch Nazi party

Oma grandmother

Oom uncle

Opa grandfather

Pieterbaas Black Peter

Rood red

Sinterklaas Santa Claus

Speculaas spiced cookies or cake in the shape of people or animals

Stoep stoop

Taai-Taai literally, tough-tough, a kind of tough, figure-shaped, cherry cake

Tante aunt

Tweede Kamer Second Chamber, lower house of the Dutch Congress

Vader father

Water-linie a belt of inundated land

Westermarkt West Market

Wit white

Zaal large room, hall

Zeedijk Seawall, a street in Amsterdam near the harbor

Zuiderzeedijk (*Zuiderzee*) South Sea, a large salt water lake, cut off from the North Sea by the largest dike in the world

Zwart black